ISDN PLANNING

AND

NETWORKING PRODUCTS

A MANAGER'S GUIDE

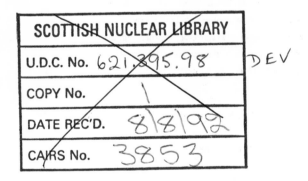
Mario Devargas
Senior Consultant
The National Computing Centre Ltd.

British Library Cataloguing in Publication Data

Devargas,   Mario

A manager's guide to ISDN : planning and
networking products

I. Title

621.382

ISBN 1-85554-149-1

© NCC CONSULTANCY1991

First published in 1991 by NCC Blackwell Ltd
108 Cowley Road, Oxford
OX4 1JF, England.

Editorial Office: The National Computing
Centre Limited, Oxford House,
Oxford Road, Manchester M1 7ED, England

Designed by Bare Facts, Creative Lynx Partnership & NCC

Printed in Great Britain by Athenaeum Press Ltd, Newcastle upon Tyne.

ISBN-1-85554-149-1

Acknowledgements

The NCC Management Reports Series has been produced as part of a major three-year Communications Programme, which has backing from the Department of Trade and Industry and British Telecom. For further information please fill in the enquiry card enclosed at the rear of the publication.

NCC would like to thank the following people for their help and assistance in the development of this report:

Edward Anderson (Digital Equipment Co. Ltd.)

Phil Barton (Digital Equipment Co. Ltd.)

Ian Benton (NCC-Communications and Security)

Chris Bruce (Ericsson Ltd.)

James Donald (Midland Bank PLC)

Martin Gronow (NCC-Communications and Security)

David Langley (Gandalf Digital Communications Ltd.)

David Pratt (International Business Machines UK Ltd.)

Andrew Richardson (ICI Corporate Management Services)

Nigel Smith (Data and Control Equipment Ltd.)

Bill Taylor (NCC-Communications and Security)

Special thanks are due to Jackie Batstone for her meticulous reading of the draft report.

The Communications Insight Series

This is one of a series of reports from a two year Communications Programme which has been funded by the Department of Trade and Industry and British Telecom, and undertaken by NCC's Communication and Security Division. The objectives of the Programme, which runs until May 1992, are to:

- raise levels of awareness within small to medium enterprises of the new and developing communications technologies now available;

- promote the effective uptake of these technologies.

The Communications Insight Series has been produced to provide senior executives, IT managers, telecommunications managers and technical support staff with:

- a state-of-the-art perspective of the new communications technologies;

- details of innovative ways in which the new technologies may be applied;

- detailed investigations of how they can be successfully integrated with existing technologies.

The reports which make up the series are:

ISDN Planning and Networking Products - A Manager's Guide

Management and Development of Communications Networks

Mobile Data Communications - Choices and Opportunities

ISDN Applications

Guide to a Mobile Europe

ISDN Terminal Product Profile

Contents

Contents

Author's biography

Mario Devargas is a Senior Consultant within NCC Consultancy and has extensive IT experience as a user, as a consultant and in various management and marketing functions. He has worked for a variety of organisations, including two computer manufacturers, a software house, a communications component manufacturer, a consultancy, and several end-user organisations in the finance and manufacturing sectors.

Mario is the author of several management guides and reports including *Introducing the Information Centre, EDI & Security*, and *Smart Cards and Memory Cards*.

1 Management overview

Network implementers have long cherished the concept of a communications medium capable of handling speech, computer data or images simultaneously. The benefits of this are readily apparent; ease of planning for future requirements, a standard interface for all media and the possibility of reducing operating costs through network rationalisation.

The interest from larger organisations in integrated communications networking has been a significant factor throughout the eighties. Unfortunately pioneering any new service requires manufacturers, suppliers and customers spending considerable amounts of time and money on market research, design, testing, implementation and marketing. With inadequate demand there is little supply while limited availability restricts the growth in demand. Consequently early integrated network offerings appeared to attract far less interest than the concept really deserved.

There are two major tendencies in the communications industry that are shaping its future: deregulation and the increasing dependency of every business on the communications infrastructure.

Within this development the communications world has retained its interest in multi-media transmission despite a difficult start. Furthermore, integrated networking technology now appears to be on the brink of a much deserved "coming of age".

These integrated digital networks herald an unparalleled growth in hi-tech communications products and services offering, within this century, the possibility of transmitting every form of known human communication "person-to-person" across the entire globe.

This state-of-the-art report examines the services, the applications, the components, and the suppliers of ISDN technology to assist all would-be implementors of integrated communications networks.

The objective of this Management Report is to describe the ISDN services and applications in relation to some of the basic questions potential users are asking themselves:

- What is ISDN?

- Why would I need to use ISDN?

- What innovative applications could be used via ISDN?

- What are the existing services in the UK and Europe?

- How much is ISDN?

- Do I need special wiring?

- Who are the UK suppliers of ISDN equipment?

- What ISDN equipment is available today?

- What role could ISDN play within my organisation?

- If I start using ISDN today, what future developments can I expect to see?

- Is my organisation too small to benefit from ISDN?

- Is my organisation too large to benefit from ISDN?

- What do I need to do to start implementing ISDN within my organisation?

These questions and many more will be discussed directly or indirectly within the pages of this report. This Management Report stems from the work NCC is conducting as part of a £1.25 million Communications Programme. It will discuss those management issues that are vital when considering the implementation and usage of ISDN, and has been structured to address two distinct management areas:

Business Management; The objective associated with this management function is to control and plan the future strategy of the company as a whole.

Technical Management; The objective associated with this area of management is to manage the day-to-day running of the company's telecommunications infrastructure.

This report can be read by all who have an interest in ISDN, from Directors and Senior Executives who have strategic responsibilities to Telecommunications Managers. The following diagrammatic description displays the author's perception of what areas of the report would be of interest to the Business Managers (B.Mgrs), Technical Managers (T.Mgrs) or both.

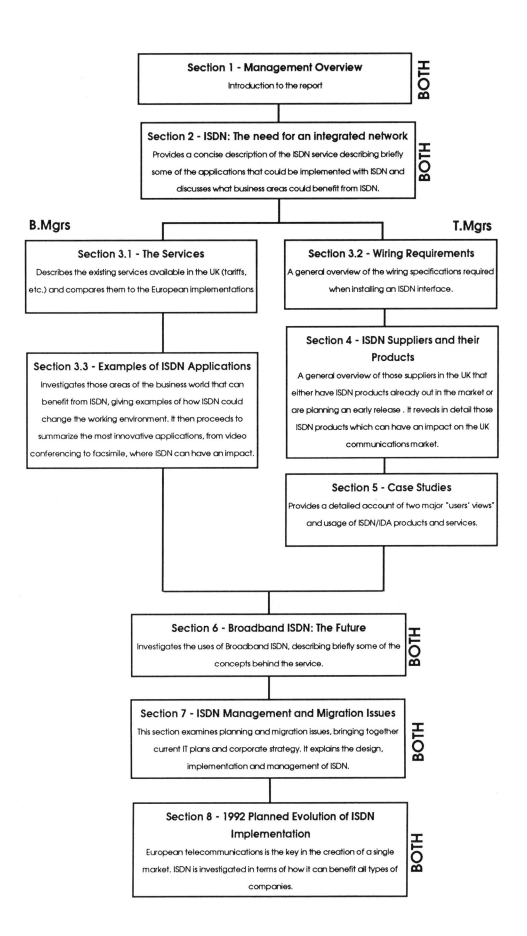

Section 1 - Management Overview

Introduction to the report

BOTH

Section 2 - ISDN: The need for an integrated network

Provides a concise description of the ISDN service describing briefly some of the applications that could be implemented with ISDN and discusses what business areas could benefit from ISDN.

BOTH

B.Mgrs   **T.Mgrs**

Section 3.1 - The Services

Describes the existing services available in the UK (tariffs, etc.) and compares them to the European implementations

Section 3.2 - Wiring Requirements

A general overview of the wiring specifications required when installing an ISDN interface.

Section 3.3 - Examples of ISDN Applications

Investigates those areas of the business world that can benefit from ISDN, giving examples of how ISDN could change the working environment. It then proceeds to summarize the most innovative applications, from video conferencing to facsimile, where ISDN can have an impact.

Section 4 - ISDN Suppliers and their Products

A general overview of those suppliers in the UK that either have ISDN products already out in the market or are planning an early release . It reveals in detail those ISDN products which can have an impact on the UK communications market.

Section 5 - Case Studies

Provides a detailed account of two major "users' views" and usage of ISDN/IDA products and services.

Section 6 - Broadband ISDN: The Future

Investigates the uses of Broadband ISDN, describing briefly some of the concepts behind the service.

BOTH

Section 7 - ISDN Management and Migration Issues

This section examines planning and migration issues, bringing together current IT plans and corporate strategy. It explains the design, implementation and management of ISDN.

BOTH

Section 8 - 1992 Planned Evolution of ISDN Implementation

European telecommunications is the key in the creation of a single market. ISDN is investigated in terms of how it can benefit all types of companies.

BOTH

2 ISDN - The need for an integrated communications network

Imagine a multi-national company with locations in America, Europe, Asia, Africa and business interests throughout the world. Then imagine the amount of local and long-distance communications it generates in a typical day: several thousand telephone calls, countless megabytes of computer data to be transmitted, thousands of telexes, hundreds of facsimile transmissions, a significant amount of high-resolution graphics and even the occasional video conferencing requirement. The following list identifies just a few of the diverse communications media involved in operating a business today:

- Speech

- Computer data

- Video

- Telex

- Facsimile

- High-resolution graphics and images

- Pagers

- Cellular phones

- Mobile radio

- Voice messaging systems

Add to this the requirements of many other organisations, large and small, and we have generated a need to transmit billions of binary ones and zeros accurately, securely, cost-effectively and on time throughout the entire world. Clearly the choice of a networking platform is crucial to the success of communications on this scale of operation.

Traditional networking techniques treat voice, data and image communication as separate entities, relying on a diverse collection of analogue and digital technologies, e.g. the PSTN for providing switched circuits for voice and data, leased line sevices for permanent circuits and for high ca-pacity/high speed digital circuits for data and voice and Public Data Networks for X.25 data trans-mission. In addition to the complex problem of having to apply several of these services to achieve an overall communications solution, many of the older type services could not deliver high speed quality transmission.

It is understandable, therefore, that much thought and research have been applied to the development of a modern high speed multi-media network. ISDN is one result of this search and is based on the concept of a single digital service capable of the accurate, efficient, secure, cost-effective and timely handling of any communications requirement.

But what is ISDN? - This acronym stands for "Integrated Services Digital Network" and can be a little misleading to users, as it is not the Services that are integrated but the Digital Network over which these services will be offered. The International Consultative Committee on Telegraphy and Telephony (CCITT) definition of ISDN is:

" *a network, evolved from the telephone integrated digital network, that provides end-to-end digital connections to support a wide range of services, including voice and non-voice and which users will have access by a limited set of standard multi-purpose customer interfaces"*

This definition covers all three types of ISDN:

- Narrowband Basic Rate Access (BRA) ISDN

- Narrowband Primary Rate Access (PRA) ISDN

- Broadband ISDN

Narrowband ISDN is based on 64 Kbps circuit switched bearer channels, with BRA providing 2B+D capacity and PRA 30B+D capacity (See Fig.1).

BASIC RATE ACCESS (2B+D) - 144K bit/s

PRIMARY RATE ACCESS (30B+D) - 2M bit/s

Figure 1 Basic and Primary Access ISDN

BRA provides 144 Kbps to the user for data and control signalling, and, allowing for the normally unseen timing and control information, actually takes about 192 Kbps of bandwidth to transmit. Basic access is designed to interface with terminals, telephones, PCs etc.

PRA is equivalent to being given a 2.048 Mbps Megastream-style line and splitting it into 30 64 Kbps B-channels, a signalling or D-channel, running at 64 Kbps and reserving the remaining 64 Kbps for synchronisation, framing etc. Primary Access is designed to interface with PABXs, multiplexors, computers etc.

Broadband ISDN is still under investigation and about fifteen to twenty years away. The technology utilised will probably be optical fibre with speeds from 150 Mbps to 600 Mbps. For more information on this technology please refer to Section 6.

ISDN has not been created to be a static product. The ISDN we can buy today is unlikely to be the same as that which we will buy in the future. The evolution of ISDN began some years ago with the conversion of the PTTs' network from analogue to digital. The next stage in this evolution will be to convert the switching nodes from analogue to digital. Later, there may be the offer of digital access to users at the periphery of the network.

This evolutionary process brings with it some very important user concerns:

- The lack of good planning information for users.

- How can users exploit ISDN to their best advantage?

- Will users be able to decide WHEN to Migrate to ISDN?

- User's requirement are not being solicited.

- Key players (from PTTs to manufacturers) are not coordinating their plans. Users do not wish to have any one supplier dominate the market and hence be tied to him for products and support.

- Unreasonably high tariff structure, leading to a loss of potential short-term business benefits.

The first two concerns will be addressed in this report. The remainder are totally dependent on the evolution of the ISDN market.

3 ISDN - today's reality

3.1 The services

The Integrated Services Digital Network (ISDN) concept and associated standards have been around since the early seventies but until recently little of this found its way into the marketplace.

Despite ISDN being seen mainly as a public networking service, many organisations, disappointed with the early commercial offerings, decided to implement their own integrated networks based on high-speed digital circuits and Time Division Multiplexing (TDM) equipment. This situation now appears to be changing and PTTs throughout the world are actively promoting public ISDN networks. As the choice of public or private network is made by evaluating the costs and availability, much attention will be focused on the rate of ISDN implementation, geographic coverage and, last but by no means least, tariff structure.

3.1.1 British Telecom (BT)

BT offer two types of ISDN service, namely ISDN2 and ISDN30. The predecessor to these, the Integrated Digital Access (IDA) service, was introduced in 1985 as a pilot single-line access operating at a non standard rate of 80 Kbps rate. This bandwidth was assigned to three channels. The Primary channel provided 64 Kbps telephony or data, the Secondary channel provided 8 Kbps data and the "D" channel provided 8 Kbps for DASS signalling.

In October 1988, BT introduced a multi-line ISDN service then known as Multi-line IDA, now renamed ISDN30 because this Primary Rate Access offers 30 independent 64 Kbps telephony or data user channels and operates at a total information rate of 2.048 Mbps. Of the remaining two 64 Kbps channels, one is used for carrying the DASS 2 (Digital Access Signalling System No. 2) signalling and the other is used for synchronisation purposes.

ISDN2 was initially launched in April 1990 as a CCITT conformant Basic Rate Access service, offering a total information rate of 144 Kbps.

ISDN2 was compatible with IDA and likewise the bandwidth is assigned into three channels. Each of the bearer channels provide telephony or data at 64 Kbps and the third channel supports signalling at 16 Kbps. ISDN2 utilises the CCITT Q.931 standard between the customer and BT network. Once inside the BT network, however, the signalling reverts to its proprietary DASS2 standard. BT have committed themselves to a European Memorandum of Understanding that requires them to adopt the CCITT Q.931 signalling standards by 1992/3.

3.1.2 Mercury Communications

Currently Mercury's ISDN service marketed as 2100 Premier, offers Primary Rate Access only and there are no immediate plans to offer basic rate access.

The 2100 Premier service supports Channel Associated Signalling (CAS) providing digital access from a DASS 2 compatible PBX to the public switched network. CAS supports voice signalling only and is seen by Mercury as a migration to systems such as DASS 2 that support ISDN features and applications across the Mercury network.

3.1.3 International ISDN

Following the 1989 EC backed Memorandum of Understanding (MoU), progress has been made throughout Europe on the introduction of ISDN services. France, West Germany, Belgium and the UK have all introduced commercial services.

Denmark, Ireland, the Netherlands and Spain have launched experimental systems whilst Italy, Greece and Portugal plan to launch some form of ISDN before 1992.

The United Kingdom

Currently international interworking on a commercial basis exists between the UK and the following countries: Australia, Belgium, Denmark, Finland, France, Germany, Hong Kong, Japan, The Netherlands, Singapore, Sweden and the USA.

France Telecom

France Telecom have been developing many major applications in collaboration with French industrial partners. Pilot Services have been available since 1988, with nationwide coverage since early 1990. Initially, when the French ISDN service was launched, there were sixty partnerships of which half are still very active. The applications cover enhancement of videotex through transfer of quality images, consultation of documents or photographic data banks, electronic mail transfer, buying through electronic catalogue as well as EDI and CAD and drawing transfer.

Germany - Bundespost

The Bundespost is following a similar strategy to France Telecom. It introduced ISDN in 1988 as a pilot service with nationwide coverage planned by 1993. There are currently 50 partnership projects with grants for user CPE purchase. The ISDN applications used in Germany are the transmission of faster Teletex (25 times faster) and Videotex (50 times faster) Services, the use of videophones for software project coordination and the use of a branch sales information system in a drug store chain.

Belgian Regie T T

RTT has been offering a limited ISDN service since mid-89, with nationwide coverage planned by 1993. The network consists of three exchanges located in Brussels.

Japan

The connection charge is free if existing PSTN lines are being replaced. In Japan, ISDN tariffs are cheaper than low use leased lines. This service is now offered nationwide with 120 international users. ISDN is being used in banks for monitoring Automated Teller Machines (ATMs), as a delivery vehicle for news articles, for remote proof reading and the inter-networking of Local Areas Networks (LANs).

3.1.4 Tariffs

The United Kingdom
British Telecom

The following charges are taken from BT's "ISDN Tariffs Sheet" and "Summary of charges for Telecommunications Service".

Please note that the charges listed here relate only to the provision of BT ISDN2 and ISDN30 services and the supply of Network Terminating Equipment. All charges are exclusive of VAT and are subject to change.

Line charges

	ISDN2	ISDN30(30 lns)	ISDN30(Nxt 30)
Connection	£400.00	£950.55	£950.55
Quarterly Rntl	£ 84.00	£801.00	£801.00
Call Charge	£ 0.352	£ 0.352	£ 0.352

Where analogue lines exist and there is spare capacity in a suitable local cable, the connection charge is reduced to £500 for each multiple of 30 digital exchange lines.

International data calls

Network	Time allowed for 4.4p.	Approx. charge/min.
France	3.11 secs.	£0.85
USA	1.89 secs.	£1.40
Japan	0.93 secs.	£2.84

Calls between UK ISDN customers and AT&T customers connected at 56K bit/s will require rate adaption. This is achieved through a device which must be purchased separately for use in conjunction with the terminal equipment.

Mercury - 2100 premier service

	First 30 Lines	Next 30 Lines
Connection	£2500.00	£800.00
Quarterly Rental	£577.50	£577.50
Call Charge	£0.333	£0.333

Where suitable lines already exist and there is spare capacity in a suitable local cable, the connection charge is reduced to £800 for each multiple of 30 digital exchange lines.

France Telecom

Connection	FF670
Quarterly Rental	FF300
Traffic Charge	1 and 1.8 x analogue

West Germany - Bundespost

Connection Basic Access	DM 130
Connection Primary Access	DM 200
Quarterly Rental Basic Access	DM 74
Quarterly Rental Primary Access	DM 518

Belgian Regie T T

Connection Basic Access	14,280F
Connection Primary Access	470,050F
Quarterly Rental Basic Access	8,389F
Quarterly Rental Primary Access	100,674F

Japan Telecommunications Co.

Connection	276 YEN
Quarterly Rental	20 YEN

If we compare these tariffs with British Telecom, the BT pricing strategy as stated on page 20 is similar to that of the Deutch Bundespost; the latter prices its ISDN service at the same rates as conventional analogue calls and carries a monthly charge of DM74.

In conclusion, France leads in high value applications and non-voice usage, with Japan leading in the deployment of Group IV facsimiles. Germany is beginning to offer partnerships, while in the UK, although there has been a late start to these services the potential for fast deployment is evident.

3.2 Wiring requirements

3.2.1 ISDN2 linebox

BT's ISDN2 service is accessed by the customer through a device called the ISDN2 Linebox, i.e. the NTE. This box, which measures about 12 x 30 x 4 cm, is wall-mounted and is equipped with two RJ45 sockets (as specified by ISO 8877:1987) which each provide a CCITT I.420 S/T customer interface. The sockets are electrically in parallel so they can *both* provide access to either or both of the ISDN2 B-channels.

The ISDN2 Linebox also includes a customer-removable cover, which allows access to Insulation Displacement Connection (IDC) blocks which, in turn, allows the connection of customer wiring.

Removal of the ISDN2 Linebox cover also gives access to a slide switch marked L (long) and S (short), and two movable links (for selecting termination resistors). The functions of the switch and links will be described shortly.

The RJ45 sockets and the IDC block mark the boundary of the 'liberalised' area. This means that the customer is at liberty to attach any of the recommended wiring configurations described below, or any British Approvals Board for Telecommunications (BABT) approved terminal, into the sockets.

3.2.2 Customer wiring

For technical reasons, there is a limited number of wiring configurations that can be achieved using the ISDN2 Linebox. These are categorised into short and long distances, with the switch in the S and the L position respectively. All ISDN2 cabling must be installed to BS6701 Part 1 (Code of Practice for Installation of Apparatus for Connection to Certain Telecommunications Systems).
To achieve reliable performance at the cable lengths described below, BT recommends the use of 8-wire unscreened twisted pair cable to the CW1700 specification, as used in BT's Open Systems Cabling Architecture (OSCA) structured cabling portfolio.

Short configurations

These configurations are used with the switch in the S or Short position. (See Fig.2).

No wiring

Without any additional wiring, a maximum of two terminals can be connected directly to the Linebox. The terminals cannot be further than their 3m connecting cords. In this configuration, the links are in the IN position because the customer wiring is terminated "IN" the linebox. Allocation of channels to the terminals is performed by the linebox.

Point to point

This option allows the customer to attach up to 150m of cable to the IDC blocks. The end of the cable must be terminated with a 'Type 2' socket containing two termination resistors. Because the line is terminated outside the linebox, the links are set to the OUT position.

This arrangement allows up to four terminals to be attached: two at the linebox and two at the Type 2 socket. The number of B-channels permits a maximum of two out of the four terminals to communicate at any one time. (The two terminals can only communicate with each other by using one channel each while connected over the ISDN). The linebox manages contention for channel usage by the terminals.

Point to multipoint

In this configuration, up to eight terminals can be attached to a 150m (maximum) cable which, in this instance, is called the "passive" or "S" bus. Each terminal is connected to the bus through a 'Type 1' socket containing a single RJ45. Each 'Type 1' socket must be electrically in parallel with the others, and can be attached either directly to the bus via its IDC block, or via a 1m (maximum) cable spur connected to a block terminal on the bus.

Any number of Type 1 sockets can be directly attached to the bus, but only eight spur arrangements are permitted. In either case, a maximum of eight terminals can be connected at any given time, but only two terminals can communicate simultaneously. The end of the cable must be terminated with a Type 2 socket and so the links in the linebox must be set to the OUT position.

Long configurations

These configurations are used with the switch in the L, or Long, position.

Point to point

A maximum cable length of 800m, terminated with a Type 2 socket, is achievable using this set up. The links inside the Linebox must be in the OUT position. The drawback to using the long length of cable is that only one terminal can be plugged into the Type 2 socket, and no terminals can be plugged into the Linebox.

Point to multipoint

BT are currently investigating the possibility of trading-off customer cable length with the number of terminals which can be attached to the cable. To date, there are no public results of these tests.

ISDN2 and structured cabling

For regulatory and technical reasons, it is currently necessary for all cables carrying ISDN2 signals to be segregated from other cables carrying telecommunications and data signals. For the time being, it is therefore essential to distribute ISDN2 using its own dedicated system. However, ISDN2 cables may run in the same trunking as other data communication cables.

At present, it is not certain as to what extent customer wiring topologies (as described above) can be incorporated into typical structured cabling schemes. Furthermore, it is unclear to what extent existing customer wiring can be upgraded to carry ISDN2 signals.

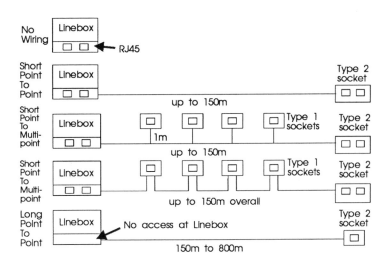

Figure 2   ISDN Customer Premises Wiring

BT has put in place a detailed programme of testing to establish firm technical parameters so that ISDN wiring can be brought into BT's OSCA portfolio.

AT&T's Systimax Premises Distribution System (PDS) has an open architecture that is compliant with the CCITT standards for ISDN. A number of sites in North America are using Systimax PDS to deliver ISDN to the desk and there is no reason why this should not be the case in the UK.

3.3 Examples of ISDN applications

Critics of ISDN often ask "Who needs ISDN anyway?" arguing that anything ISDN can do can also be achieved using existing communications technology.   This may be true, but ISDN allows for many potentially exciting new forms of communication as well as revitalising some tried and tested applications.   ISDN will come of age by proving itself to be the ideal technology platform for the communications networks of the future. Why should this be so? One strong argument for ISDN lies in its integration capabilities. Many of today's communications products are firmly compartmentalised. For instance, a LAN is not often seen as having potential voice transmission technology, while little has been done to develop the "telephone handset" into a personal communicator concept, offering data and graphics transmission. ISDN is well placed to bring about a quite radical rethinking of many of our stereotyped ideas on communications.

Clearly, this change is not going to happen overnight and in the interim ISDN will mainly be offering a better way to handle existing applications. As a service offering high speed and reliable transmission, ISDN is well suited to supporting a variety of communications requirements not easily or cost-effectively catered for by existing network technology. The following applications are just some examples of the uses of the ISDN today and possibly in the future:

- Video conferencing

- Monitoring and Surveillance

- Visual Telephony

- Personal Computer Conferencing

- TeleMarketing

- Telematics - High-speed facsimile

- Telematics - Videotex

- Document image processing

Vertical market applications

To show how these applications may fit into the business environment, below is a three-dimensional diagram that relates the application areas identified in this report to some business sectors and functions.

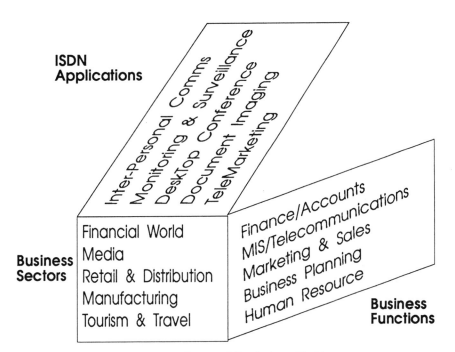

Figure 3 Relationship Between ISDN Applications and the Business World

If we examine Fig.3 more closely, we can investigate each business sector in terms of the demands it makes on the communications industry:

Financial environment (banks, dealers, etc.)

This sector is concerned with a variety of issues, such as the provision of advanced banking services to domestic users, corporate banking services, collaborative dealing and personal insurance services. (Note: The data speeds required at the user's premises for some services in this sector are likely to vary enormously - simple text and data will not require high rates but will require particular call types, e.g. fast set-up time and high integrity/security.)

Media environment (publishers, tv, etc.)

The media, publishing and advertising sector has been using telecommunications tools for some time and will probably be at the forefront of any new telecommunications usage. ISDN could play a major role in the further development of the media sector by providing the means of mass multimedia dissemination of information and entertainment, providing broadband integrated communication facilities for "on-the-spot" news coverage and by enabling access to and the linking together of multimedia databases.

Retail & distribution environment

The demand for good communications is increasing in the retail and distribution industries, the main reason being the broadening of their market-scope, implying that products will be sourced from a wide geographical area.

"Just-in-time" (JIT) methodology is being implemented to deliveries as a method of controlling stores and quality in the local supermarkets and shops. JIT refers to the ability to produce minimal-sized batches of finished goods only when needed, i.e. responding to the market "forces". Hence in the retail trade it is applied to keeping adequate amounts of stock at all times.

Home shopping, electronic catalogue shopping and the training of retail personnel will be some of the "products" offered by these companies when they have access to multimedia databases and face-to-face communications.

Tourism & travel environment

The phenomenal growth in the transportation of people and freight has not diminished since the early 1970s and will probably continue. Associated with this movement of people and goods is the transmission of information in the form of text, images and data.

There already exist sophisticated booking and reservation systems providing up-to-date information about routes, schedules, tariffs, etc. The main questions here are: Will the existing communications capacity be able to cope with the increase in volume envisaged? Furthermore, with the use of an integrated service, what other applications could be of great use to this industry?

ISDN applications can support this industry by providing rapid image and data transmission facilities, access to multimedia databases, remote surveillance and telemarketing systems. Some of these are: remote inspection of aircraft or damaged goods, telemarketplace for freight and transport and airport teleshopping.

Manufacturing environment

Within this industry, communications already hold the key in supplying the customer with the quality, delivery and services they demand. Further advances in the communications field will help the manufacturing sector by:

- providing the capability of transmitting large amounts of graphical data internationally (e.g. CAD);

- providing access to multimedia design and component databases;

- providing face-to-face communications for collective decision-making, negotiation, training and remote surveillance;

- improving factory-floor communications, interfacing with MAP and TOP.

Some examples of applications are: a product library, remote control diagnosis and maintenance.

The following sub-sections look at each application mentioned on page 28, defining each application area and discusses typical uses.

3.3.1 Video conferencing

Video conferencing is a mode of simultaneous, interactive, sight and sound digital communication in colour. This communications tool will help companies in holding meetings, conferences, training, interviews, etc., without the participants travelling to a central location.

The main benefits include:

- **Enhanced executive productivity**

- **Improved 'communications' speed**

- **Improved quality of decisions as a consequence of the multi-media environment**

- **Savings on travel costs**

- **Augmented overall level of communications within a group of professionals.**

For this tool to be of benefit it must have the following features:

Automated Camera Positioning	**This produces a natural flow to the video conference by auto-matically concentrating on the speaker.**
High Resolution Still Graphics	**This permits the display of overheads, 35mm slides, photographs and diagrams during video conference.**
White Board Camera	**Transmits information written on the white board.**
VCR Play & Record	**Tapes the conference for future playbacks.**
Automatic Dialling	**Automatically dials remote locations and sets up the conference.**
Encryption	**Scrambles signals to provide security.**
PAL-to-NTSC Conversion	**Room is compatible with local standards.**

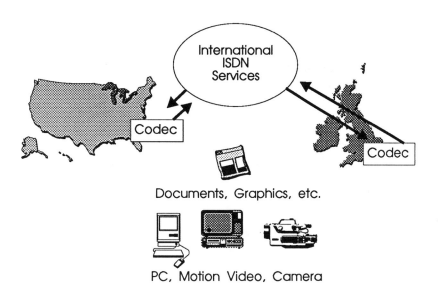

Documents, Graphics, etc.

PC, Motion Video, Camera

Figure 4 Video Conferencing

Figure 4 illustrates an international video conference session between the UK and the USA. The process of using ISDN internationally means that the user is responsible for "rate adaption" if the ISDNs are different, for example between the USA and the UK. In the UK, BT's ISDN runs on 64 Kbps with 8 bits/sample under CCITT A-Law encoding format, while in the USA ISDN runs on 56 Kbps with 7 bits/sample under Mu-Law encoding format.

3.3.2 Monitoring and surveillance

Organisations with a requirement to monitor and control remote systems, e.g. hospitals for the monitoring of patients; defence; water authorities and chemical processing plants, are all likely to benefit from ISDN.

Performance monitoring and measurement will be greatly improved because of the availability of large amounts of bandwidth which can be dialled up economically and on demand. This will provide an ideal platform for telemetry applications such as CCTV, process control, alarm systems, fault diagnosis and fault rectification. Other examples include security surveillance of property, monitoring of remote unmanned industrial sites, observation and control of traffic, remote monitoring of medical conditions (see Fig.5).

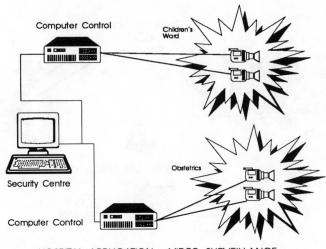

HOSPITAL APPLICATION - VIDEO SURVEILLANCE

Figure 5   Monitoring and Surveillance

The basic components of such a system, for example, for use in video surveillance could be:

- Video cameras distributed in a controlled environment

- Remote tele-surveillance system (a black box to which video cameras are connected)

- Central command processor (a personal computer).

3.3.3 Visual telephony

Visual telephony, i.e. the simultaneous transmission of moving images and voice, may soon become a reality. The prediction being made in some knowledgeable circles is that by 1993 terminals with built-in video codecs will start to appear in the business sector and that by 1998 videophones will start to appear in the home (see Fig.6).

Four essential steps are required for the effective implementation of this service:

1   A digital compression technique for the effective utilization of reduced bandwidth transmission

2   The use of standards, so that both parties can understand the coding algorithm utilized on their video codecs (coder/decoders) machines

3   The use of Very Large Scale Integration (VLSI) technology. This is needed due to the enormous complexity of compression algorithms utilized. It requires a vast amount of complicated electronic circuitry

4   Network availability.

Therefore with ISDN providing the bandwidth, recent improvements in signal compression techniques offering the technical ability; all that is now required is a significant reduction in the price of codecs and carrier services!

Figure 6   Visual Telephony

3.3.4 Personal computer (PC) conferencing

PC conferencing can permit concurrent voice (e.g. via one "B" channel) and data (e.g. information and graphical images via the another "B" channel) calls between various PCs running a multitasking operating system, e.g. OS/2.

The system becomes a conference due to the fact that up to eight subscribers can talk and pass information to each other in real-time using standard PC programs (see Fig.7).

This system is based around the concept of cooperative computing combining people-to-people and people-to-computer communications.

The PC must be fitted with a basic rate ISDN adapter, a digital telephone and a mouse/light pen (used to amend diagrams or pictures).

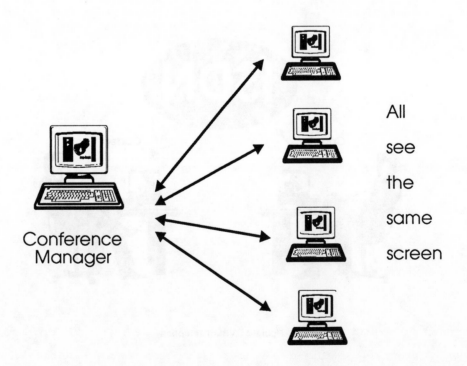

Figure 7   DeskTop Conferencing

The characteristics of such a system could be:

- Automatic screen image transfer

- Work Space available on the screen for discussion

- Background File Transfer capability

- Transfer of Keyboard/Screen Control; this is useful, for example, in a training session

- Conference management, so that one subscriber can control the session. This ensures that each conference is managed by a nominated participant who acts as "chairperson" and ensures that file transfers are kept to a required minimum. This means that a pseudo-"real-time" environment can be maintained

- Interface to different sources of data, e.g. Mainframe, scanners, facsimiles, etc.

3.3.5 Telemarketing

This application combines telecommunications, automatic call management and the human marketing agent so as to improve productivity in managing incoming calls (see Fig.8).

The aim of this system will be for the telephonist to obtain the required information from the caller via his Calling Line Identity (CLI) (e.g. Company name, address, telephone number, etc.) at the same time as the call is been answered. This obviously will reduce the "talk-time" in the data collection process and hence increase the number of calls handled by the agent.

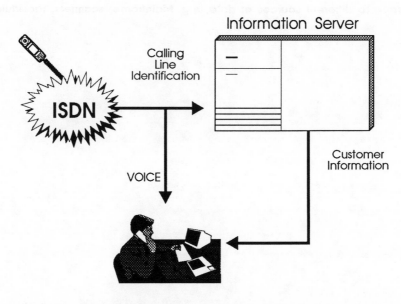

TeleMarketing via ISDN

Figure 8   Marketing

The following are some applications that could be supported from this type of system:

- Customised call processing, allowing the receptionist to identify the clients instantly and hence being able to redirect the call quickly

- The collection of advertising demographic data from a media campaign. This system can track caller responses and record the results of an advertisement in real time

- Dealer/engineer locator application. This system will display the nearest dealer/engineer at the start of the conversation, hence eliminating the data gathering and host response time normally required to display the information.

3.3.6 Telematics - high-speed facsimile

The facsimile machine has firmly established itself since the early 1970s as a permanent part of the daily business environment. Presently the facsimile is used in over 80% of UK's medium and large size companies, with demand in the small businesses increasing at a staggering rate.

A facsimile machine converts an image into electrical impulses suitable for transmission over the public networks. When it receives an image, the machine de-crypts it and produces the output, usually on paper.

The facsimile services offered prior to digital transmission are automatic/manual dialled call and auto-answer. This type of service has been available for many years but has suffered from a lack of standardisation and the limitations of the analogue telephone network.

With the advent of digital transmission and CCITT standards, the services offered over ISDN could be in addition to the existing services: delayed delivery, multiple destination and code, speed and format conversion for different terminals.

The CCITT recommendations for facsimile machines are:

Group 1   **Analogue transmission taking about 6 minutes for an A4 page of text.**

Group 2   **Analogue transmission taking about 3 minutes for an A4 page of text.**

Group 3   **Using Digital transmission with a resolution of 200x200 pels/inch taking about 1 minute.**

Group 4   **Using digital transmission with a range of resolution from 200 to 400 pels/inch operating at about 10–20 secs. Group 4 machines require a higher bandwidth and will probably be the standard used over ISDN giving higher speed, quality and volumes.**

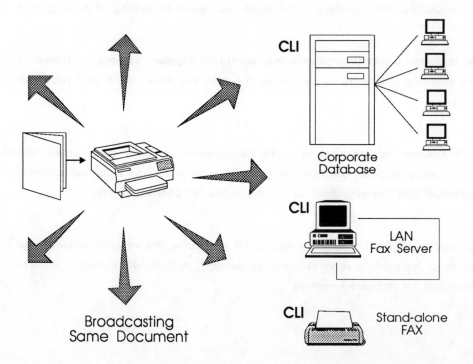

Figure 9 Telematics .. Facsimile

As Fig.9 shows, a graphical document can be broadcast via ISDN due to each subscriber having his own CLI. Furthermore, due to ISDN's integration capabilities, the facsimile document can be distributed to separate machines.

3.3.7   Telematics - videotex

This application is defined as an interactive information retrieval service. The user, usually via a hand-held remote control device, makes an inquiry of a central database. The service responds in approximately a second with a page of data transmitted at about 9.6 Kbps. This application, although still somewhat primitive, is being used today by TV companies as a news and general information dissemination service.

With ISDN this service can be expanded to include:

- Transactions   (e.g. reservations, home-shopping)

- Messaging service between users

- Loading of software from a database to a terminal.

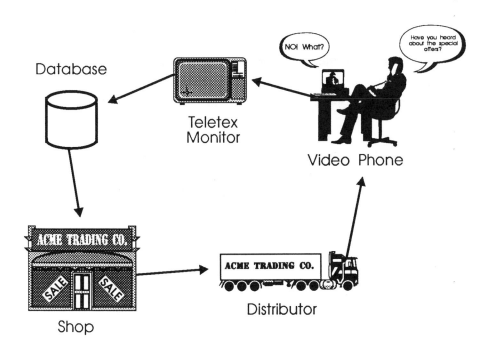

Figure 10 Telematics .. Videotex

3.3.8   Document image processing

Document Image Processing (DIP) is concerned with the capture of documents (data and images) by scanning and digitising the page images and storing them as bit-mapped files.

The basic DIP system comprises of three basic processes: input (the capturing / creating / editing of a document), storage and retrieval. All these processes require a control module and a communications infrastructure.

The communications requirements of a DIP system may include:

- Links from a host computer system to a dedicated DIP system

- Links from one DIP system to another, whether an identical system or one obtained from a different supplier

- Communications from a facsimile system to the DIP system

- Communications from one supplier's DIP system in one organisation to another supplier's DIP system in another organisation

- Links to other tools and hardware devices, e.g. multimedia databases, video etc.

DIP is very closely related to the facsimile machine discussed in Section 3.3.7, and utilises the same CCITT Standards when it comes to scanning, data compression and transmitting the documents, e.g. CCITT Group 3 and 4 standards.

The multimedia integrated environment that ISDN could offer can enhance the uses of this tool tremendously, by giving the user access to other tools but, more importantly, giving the applications the broadband required for greater speed and volume.

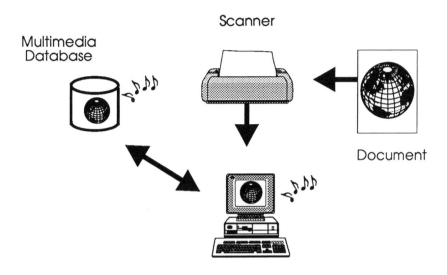

Multimedia
Database

Scanner

Document

Integrated Application
motion,voice,text & graphics

Figure 11   Document Image Processing

Some DIP applications could be:

Record management   This application is typical of a "high volume of input and a low rate of retrieval" system. It is aimed at replacing paper or microfilm records and increasing the search/retrieval rate of a record. Typical applications include police criminal records, library newspaper records, etc.

Office systems   The main aim of this system is to capture incoming paper documents, such as contracts, letters, etc. and manage them alongside documents created electronically. This type of application will become more and more popular as the price and availability of storage media becomes more amenable to the users and furthermore when the communications "capacity" is available. Typical application include a Law & Accountancy firm's management of contracts and government offices' need to manage forms, for example, the poll tax form.

Engineering Documents (CAD - Computer Aided Design)

CAD systems need specialised equipment (e.g. scanning devices, plotting equipment, big screens, etc.) which implies that a great amount of storage space is required due to the large volumes of data generated by these applications. This type of application will benefit from a multimedia environment in terms of getting the work done more effectively. For example, in a CAD group, the use of desktop-conferencing in the co-operative development of a diagram or graph is essential.

4 ISDN suppliers and their products

The communications industry is being encouraged by government and service providers to develop a range of ISDN products. Initially the availability is likely to be limited as suppliers wait for their competitors to make the first move, but roll-out will no doubt gather pace as ISDN credibility begins to grow.

This section looks at some of the ISDN products currently on the UK market and lists potential suppliers. Inclusion of a specific product or supplier should not be taken as any form of recommendation. In line with normal business 'best practice', prospective buyers of ISDN products are advised to undertake a thorough evaluation of the products before procuring any hardware or software from the supplier. The following suppliers will be discussed here:

British Telecom (BT)

Ericsson Ltd.

Eurotel Ltd.

GEC Plessey Telecommunications Ltd. (GPT)

Harris Corporation

Hayes Microcomputer Products Inc.

Hewlett Packard Ltd.

International Business Machines Ltd. (IBM)

International Computers (UK) Ltd. (ICL)

IDACOMM

Newbridge Network Ltd.

Northern Telecom

Siemens Communications Systems Ltd.

Philips Telecommunications and Data Systems

The following companies will be discussed in a more detail in Section 4.2:

General Datacomm (GDC)

Data and Control Equipment Ltd. (DCE)

Digital Equipment Co. Ltd. (DEC)

Gandalf Digital Communications Ltd.

4.1   ISDN products

4.1.1   Terminal products

British Telecom

BT X21 comms card & fast file transfer software.

This card plugs into one of the expansion slots inside an IBM PC XT/AT (or compatible) and provides access to the ISDN via the NTE4. The FFT package supports high speed file transfer and retrieval between PCs connected to the ISDN.

BT ISDN communications card

This equipment is for the Merlin M5000 Range PC/XT/AT or compatibles, and plugs into one of the expansion slots. Once a call has been set up (i.e. access to public and private ISDN services), data is transferred via the interface and handled by the card's on-board 80188 processor, leaving the whole of the PC memory map free to process the application software.

Ericsson Ltd.

Network Terminator (NT1 with "U" to "S"), IMUX (with "U" to "T" interfaces), terminal adaptors (with V & X interfaces) and telephones.

GEC Plessey Telecommunications Ltd (GPT)

GPT ISDT Digital Terminal

This terminal has simultaneous voice and data over a single pair of existing telephone wires, having an intelligent signalling technique between the ISDX and itself, thus enabling intercom call indication even when an outgoing call is being made. It displays the text message sent to the ISDT.

Hayes Microcomputer Products Inc.

Hayes ISDN PC card

This is an ISDN terminal adapter for the IBM PC and compatibles, giving the PC full access to the Basic Rate Interface (2B+D) of ISDN. This card works in much the same way as the Hayes modem, but taking advantage of the increased functionality of ISDN. Through its RJ11 jack, the card also adapts to any standard telephone to ISDN for digitised voice transmission.

International Business Machines Ltd (IBM)

IBM ISDN interface co-processor/2

This is a communications card for the IBM PS/2 Micro Channel computers, plus supporting software (IBM ISDN Co-Processor Support Program). The IBM ISDN Interface Co-Processor/2 is a full length adapter that plugs into any 16 or 32 bit expansion slot of an IBM PS/2 Model 50, 50Z, 55SX, 60, 70, P70 or 80. This interface supports two protocols on the B channels, namely SDLC and LAPB, providing access to ISDN's BRI. The user may choose to run both the B channels under SDLC, both under LAPB or one under each protocol.

International Computers (UK) Ltd. (ICL)

DRS ISDN intelligent workstation

There are three models, 10, 20 & 30, with Model 30 having all the following characteristics:

- Multi-tasking
- Voice and Data Integration
- OS/2 with Presentation manager
- Integrated Featurephone
- ISDN 2B+D Service

This workstation has been the subject of customer trials in the UK and USA, and is marketed by France Telecom in France.

4.1.2 Networking products

Ericsson Ltd.
MD110 ISPBX

This ISPBX includes ISDN support, multi-vendor PBX networking via a range of DPNSS functions and support for a variety of communications applications (for example, digital cordless telecommunications, telemarketing, etc.) as well as basic telephony functions. The MD110 provides a migration path from a private networking standard to the public ISDN environment and interfacing with ISDN2 and ISDN30 as standard.

Eurotel Ltd.
DETMUX - Digital Exchange Terminal Multiplexer

This is a software controlled primary multiplexer offering integration of voice, video, low and high speed data via a range of interfaces.

DACCS - Digital Access Cross Connect System

This is a software controlled cross connection of channels between 2.048 Mbps trunks. This component will re-route voice, 64Kbps data, or high speed Nx64 Kbps data.

DDIMUX - Digital Drop and Insert Multiplexer

DDIMUX offers drop and insert access to any number of channels in a standard G704 framed 2.048 Mbs 30/31 channel PCM system, providing full duplex communication in either direction from the DDI site.

GEC Plessey Telecommunications Ltd (GPT)
GPT ISDX Digital Exchange

The GPT ISDX system is a British designed Integrated Services PBX (ISPBX) providing 2B+D operation for Private and Public ISDN access, operating at 64Kbps or higher. It has the capacity for simultaneous voice (fully digital telephony, digitising voice signals from the handset for high quality reproduction), text & data (with speeds up to 64Kbps via X2 or V24 interfaces and access to packet switched data networks) and video transmission.

Harris Corporation

Harris 20-20 (integrated voice & data digital PABX)

Combined with the Attendant Workstation and Optic Teleset, this item provides voice and data capabilities. Both synchronous and asynchronous data communications are supported as well as modem pooling, protocol conversion (e.g. ASCII to IBM 3270 or SNA/SDLC) and X.25 packet switching interfaces. ISDN, DMI (Host) and LAN interfaces are part of the Harris 20-20 basic design structure.

Newbridge Network Ltd.

3600 MainStreet Range

This is a group of multiplexers and bandwidth managers support either primary rate (from 32 to 256 ports) or basic rate (from 12 to 15 ports) interfaces.

4600 MainStreet Range

This is a family of digital backbone network managers that integrates the management of the 3600 MainStreet series of channel banks, multiplexers and bandwidth managers together with the 2600 MainStreet series of remote Data Termination Units for the overall digital backbone network and provides an interface for their control.

Northern Telecom

Meridian SL-1 ISDN signalling link

This link provides a data link between Meridian SL-1 to ISDN, giving the customers the option to use analogue leased lines, where digital is unavailable, as well as digital leased lines. With the ISDN Signalling Link, advanced Meridian SL-1 features and services (i.e. normally associated with a single PBX) are incorporated across multiple locations.

The ISDN Signalling Link uses a dedicated channel to establish the ISDN D - channel for transmission of the ISDN Q.931 signalling protocol. The D-channel uses either a V.24 or V.35 interface at speeds from 1.2 Kbps to 64 Kbps synchronous.

Siemens Communications Systems Ltd.
MCX PABX range

The main characteristics of this system are as follows:

- Normal PBX features (e.g. digital telephones, logging, etc.)
- Automatic Call Distribution
- Mainframe Access, via a gateway
- PC to PC communications
- Packet Switching
- Modem Pooling
- Telex
- Digital Access Signalling System 2
- Digital Private Networking

HICOM300

This is a networking voice and data PABX with up to 500 extension in a single system supports DASS2 and DPNSS. The integrated server provides voice, mail, fax servers, etc.

Philips Telecommunications and Data Systems
SOPHO-S2500 - IS-PABX

This family of digital IS-PABX systems is based on ISDN standards. Its characteristics include:

- Enhanced voice facilities
- Multi-node networking
- ISDN compatibility, providing an immediate private ISDN Network, with end-to-end digital transmission via a standard interface.

The Sopho-S2500 supports a Sopho-set digitaltelephone terminal that facilitates simultaneous transmission of voice and data over a single telephone line. The system also supports a Line Adaptor Module (LAM308) that provides two 64kbits data connections over a single extension line.

Sopho extension devices may operate at distances of up to 2km from the main switch. They are based upon the standard 2B+D format (144 Kbps) BRA for digital transmission at the U-reference point.

4.1.3 TERMINAL ADAPTORS

Harris Corporation
ISDN Terminal Adaptors

These adaptors provide ISDN basic rate interface for voice and data applications.

International Business Machines Ltd (IBM)
IBM 7820 ISDN Terminal Adaptor

This stand-alone equipment allows installed IBM devices to be connected without modifications to ISDN. This terminal adaptor, with IBM Communications Network Management, provides a central management tool for both the SNA and ISDN environments. With the 7820, existing SNA communications equipment can access ISDN services through the ISDN BRI, providing 2B+D operation. This terminal adaptor provides for attachment of selected V and X series DTEs, operating in synchronous mode to ISDN BRI. In terms of interfaces it supports V24, V35 and X.21 interfaces.

International Computers (UK) Ltd. (ICL)
ISDN terminal adaptor

This unit connects an analogue voice line and an asynchronous RS232 device to a single (2B+D) line, enabling the user to retain his investment in existing equipment whilst utilising the new ISDN services. Concurrent voice and data access are supported.

Newbridge Network Ltd.
2600 Terminal Adaptor Range

These terminal adaptors have interfaces for V.24, V.35, X.21 and X.25 and can be used to connect to a private ISDN.

1600 MainStreet ISDN terminal adaptors

This is a family of network manageable ISDN terminal adaptors used for connecting RS-232/V.24, RS.449/X.21 and V.35 devices to Basic Rate Access Lines of public ISDN.

4.1.4 Test equipment

British Telecom
BT t4200 portable ISDN tester

This Basic Rate tester is the first in a family of portable testers, designed at BT's Research Labs to be used by maintenance and installation staff to functionally test ISDN installation. Its characteristics include:

- X21 leased line interfaces for B Channel error rate tests
- Simultaneous use of both B Channels
- Telephony interfaces for functional speech checks

Harris Corporation
ISDN protocol analyser

Provides a visual display of D-channel messages on layers 1, 2 and 3. The analyser also provides voice and data communications at the S-Interface.

Hewlett Packard Ltd.

HP 4954I ISDN WAN protocol analyser

This system provides the user with the extensive simulation and monitoring capabilities required to test the various layers of the ISDN implementation. Incorporated within the system is an HP 4954I ISDN channel-selector interface that gives the user the access required to test the basic rate ISDN implementation. The main product features are as follows:

- ISDN Access, analysis & simulation
- DataCommC, a multi-tasking programming language
- ISDN basic rate access
- Protocol application support for SNA/SDLC & X.25

HP 18280a ISDN basic rate monitor interface

This interface is for the HP 495A/B/C and HP 4952A WAN protocol analyser and lets the engineer make a connection into a basic rate ISDN at either the "S" or "T" interface. The D or either of the B channels can be extracted to test signalling or user data. The types of tests that can be achieved through this interface are:

- Physical interface testing
- Voice testing
- D channel signalling testing
- User data testing

HP 18270a ISDN basic rate channel access and analysis

This device adds ISDN testing capabilities to the selection of troubleshooting tools on the portable HP 4952A protocol analyser. Access to the ISDN network is provided through a hardware module, which attaches to the HP 4952A giving it the following characteristics:

- Physical layer LEDs with INFO states making it easy to determine that the line is in the proper operating state.

- Access to any of the B or D channels is provided through an auxiliary data port (RS-232/V24)

- Includes a handset to allow full duplex monitoring or voice communication over either of the B channel

- Can check user data integrity by decoding SNA, X.25, HDLC and SDLC data on the B channels or X.25 data on the D channels.

HP 18268a ISDN analysis software for the HP 4952a

This provides a software package that adds powerful ISDN D channel decoding capabilities plus full access to either of the B channel for analysis of user data.

IDACOM

the pt300 protocol conformance test system

The PT300 is a high-performance, luggable protocol tester with WAN (X.25 or SNA) and ISDN (BRI of 2B+D) interfaces. Within its array of facilities it provides for statistical analysis, performance measurements, error diagnostics and detection, line utilisation and more.

This system is the approved reference protocol tester and ISDN conformance tester for the EC.

4.1.5   Other equipment

British Telecom

BT videocodec VC 2100

This equipment compresses and digitises TV picture signals for transmission over digital networks. This device has selectable data rates of P x 64Kbit/s, where P=1 to 30, allowing users to integrate video, voice and data traffic.

Harris Corporation

ISDN traffic generator adaptor

Connects up to 48 analogue lines into a 24 dual-channel ISDN S-Interface switch.

International Business Machines Ltd (IBM)

Com300 system

This is a digital switching system with in-built ISDN switching which provides a range of facilities including voice and data messaging. The IBM Com300 system consists of products and capabilities at four different levels:

The Desk; this system offers the user telephones and terminals that will fit almost any business application. It offers digital telephones, data interfaces for personal computers, terminals and teletex terminals.

Local connections; in order to utilise all the components of the desk functions, Com300 provides connectivity to voice, data, text and image. Its internal protocols are based on evolving ISDN recommendations.

Servers; integrated into the system are a variety of computers that provide communications-oriented services to the user. These include an Administration Server, a Call Detail Server, a Voice Mail Server and a Telecommunications Server.

External connections; the Com300 has interfaces to analogue and digital trunks and tie lines, as well as ISDN lines (Basic Rate and Primary Rate). It can also connect to computer systems and public data networks.

The IBM Com300 is available in three models, all of which use the same processor, operating system, interface cards and servers. The models are:

- IBM Com300 Model 340, provides a maximum of 256 ports and can be accommodated in only one cabinet with two shelves.

- IBM Com300 Model 370, provides a maximum of 960 ports in up to 4 cabinets. Duplex processors and switching matrices are optional.

- IBM Com300 Model 390, provides a maximum of 5120 ports in up to 15 cabinets. Duplex processors and switching matrices are standard. The cabinets have additional room for power supplies, distribution frames and integrated servers.

CallPath services architecture

The CallPath services architecture defines a framework to integrate call processing functions with existing and new data processing applications. It enables communications between a computer and a telephone switch so that a host computer application can monitor and influence the action of the switch. The existing products in the services include CallPath/400; this is the fist implementation of the CallPath Services API, providing a software platform that enables applications to link the data processing power of the AS/400 system with the telephony processing capabilities of a PBX. The types of PBX it supports include IBM Com300, Siemens Hicom and Northern Telecom Meridian.

International Computers (UK) Ltd. (ICL)
DeskTop conferencing package

This system uses existing screen-based data (i.e. data from a mainframe, PC or scanner), and thus requires no software development. The package comprises:

- Digital Telephone

- PC or DRS Intelligent Workstation

- Light Pen and Mouse

- DeskTop Conferencing Software.

Newbridge Network Ltd.

5601/2 MainStreet software

Netview interface program for 4601/4602 network management software.

Northern Telecom

ISDN application protocol

This is an intelligent signalling link that sends and receives command and status messages between the Meridian SL-1 and a host computer processor. In this way the ISDN Application Protocol enables functional integration of voice and data within host computer software applications.

Meridian ISDN telephone m5317t

This unit is aimed at the executive, with the following features:

- A 2X40 character display and softkeys

- Single button feature access and indication

- Multiple directory appearances and handsfree operation.

Centrex ISDN display set m5209t

This unit is aimed at the knowledge worker and has a 2X24 display, single button feature access and multiple directory appearance. Within its specification it conforms to CCITT ISDN S/T interface connection with full 2B+D implementation. The D-Channel Protocol is X.25 PAD with X.3, X.28 and X.29.

Philips Telecommunications and Data Systems

SOPHO-SET digital telephones

These telephones (or digital voice/data-terminals) are provided with a V.24 plug for connecting a data-terminal and they communicate with the SOPHO-S digital PABX via a two-wire 2B+D line.

ISDN videophone

This videophone satisfies German PTT/Telekom requirements, and its characteristics include face-to-face telephony and the transmission of diagrams, photographs and 3-D drawings.

Pictureview

This facilites the transmission of high-resolution still pictures from a PC on one B channel while using the other B channel to discuss the contents.

4.2 Supplier commitment to ISDN

General Datacomm

General Datacomm (GDC) has been a supplier of communications systems since 1969. Initially the business operated from New York but later migrated to Connecticut and now employs two thousand people, with subsidiary organisations in Canada and the UK.

The company's first major products were modems followed by Time Division and Statistical Multiplexing (TSDM) equipment. GDC has the distinction of being the first approved supplier to connect their TDSM equipment to British Telecom's Megastream and Kilostream services and Time Division Multiplexing (TDM) remain the flagship of the company.

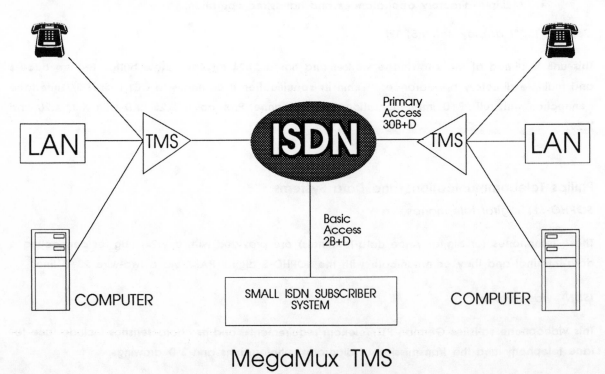

MegaMux TMS

Figure 12   General View of TMS Environment

The recent release of the Megamux TMS, successor to the Megamux II, has moved the company's TDM offerings from proprietary to European standards (see Fig.12). For example, a CEPT 2.048 Mbps standard that adheres to the CCITT G.732 frame structure. GDC's Combined Digital Aggregate (CDA) card forms the basis of their ISDN development and is seen as being the likely platform for future work in this area.

The CDA card supports 2.048 Mbps, provides two G.732 ports for drop and insert use and offers switching for individual 64 Kbps time slots. PABXs require only one G.732 interface, as communication with multiple remote nodes is achieved using channel-associated signalling (see Fig.13).

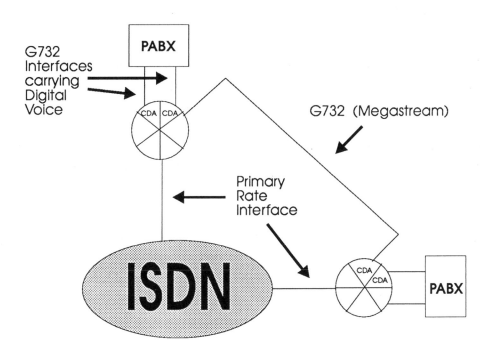

Figure 13   CDA Link

The CDA card extracts the signalling from time slot 16 and routes it through the Transport Management System (TMS) multiplexer network along with the voice circuit. Voice circuits and signalling can be automatically re-routed in case of link failure.

Compliance with international standards permits compatibility with fractional services. The major advantage of fractional services is usually cost, as the user only pays for the number of time slots which are actually required, rather than for the full 2 Mb bandwidth. Additionally, fractional services can provide extra bandwidth on demand without the need for equipment or link changes.

General Datacomm see their latest TDM products featuring the CDA card as an investment in migration to ISDN. The CDA card can fit into existing equipment to give immediate benefits as well as providing a sound platform for future ISDN implementation.

In line with other communications suppliers, General Datacomm has still to establish a firm user base for their new products within the UK.

On the International market, however, things are beginning to happen and an example of this is the recent commissioning of a multiplexer network for Bunge (Australia) Pty Ltd., to be used in conjunction with "Macrolink", Australia's primary rate ISDN service. This twelve node network uses the Megamux TMS and Megamux TMS Compact multiplexers to provide a virtual private network based on the CCITT 2Mb (30B+D) structure with standard D channel signalling. General Datacomm claim significant benefits for the network, including substantial line cost savings and resilience.

Cost savings are achieved by compression techniques, permitting a single ISDN B channel to carry three voice circuits as well as data. Resilience (and additional cost savings) is the result of the TMS Compact multiplexers automatically setting up and clearing down ISDN calls in response to commands from the TMS network management system. This means that the system can be configured to dial up ISDN bandwidth whenever a link fails, or to meet peak bandwidth demands.

Data & Control Equipment Ltd. (DCE)

DCE Communications Group was founded in 1969 and since this date has been a supplier of communications products, including facsimiles, modems and dial-up video conferencing equipment. Its Head Office is based in Aylesbury, Buckinghamshire with subsidiaries in the USA (DCE Corp) and Germany (DCE GmbH Telekommunikations-systeme).

The company's main product is the V-3100 Dial-Up Video Conferencing System, which is manufactured by PictureTel in the USA. DCE is the exclusive UK distributor of this product.

The V-3100 comprises of full Two-Way motion video, full Duplex Audio with Echo erase without needing to make the conference room acousticly sound, document and 3D object transmission, slides transmission, PC screen transmission, and video tape recording. All this is performed over two dial-up lines operating at data rates of 64Kbps.

The V-3100 incorporates the C-3000 Video Codec which is software based and uses VLSI to compress, digitise and transmit the images and sound. This codec uses its own proprietary encoding algorithms, either HVQ or from the last quarter of 1990 SG3, and will comply with the forthcoming Px64 - H.261 CCITT International Videoconferencing Standard.

According to Nigel Smith (DCE Marketing Communications Manager), PictureTel's proprietary algorithm is very efficient and fits into the next generation of encoding algorithms. DCE's comparison to other algorithms (i.e. in terms of data rates to achieve comparable picture quality) is:

PictureTel SG3	PictureTel HVQ	CCITT H261
64	112	256
128	224	448
256	392	768
384	576	1024

The driving force behind the growth of videoconferencing is due to improved compression technology, a reduction in the equipment cost through VLSI technology, digital networks (e.g. dial-up ISDN) and international standards. This has led DCE to predict their growth turnover from £17m in 1990/91 to £32m in 1991/92 and a staggering £65m in 1992/93 EC open market period.

In terms of VLSI technology, DCE are taking a further step in implementing their Codec machine on a chip. According to Steffan Ericsson (PictureTel International Marketing Director) they have gone into a joint venture with INTEL in the USA to develop a video codec on a chip that can perform about a billion operations in a second. This joint venture will see the experts in video conferencing and multimedia combining their effort and knowledge to produce tomorrow's technology.

Presently, PictureTel's client list looks like the top 20 companies in the US's Fortune 100. This includes AT&T, McDonnel Douglas, Apple, Bank of Boston, and Texaco. While in the UK via DCE, their client list includes National Westminster Bank, The Post Office, Mobil Oil, Arthur Anderson and others.

Gandalf Digital Communications Ltd

Gandalf Digital Communications was founded in 1969 in Canada and since this date has been one of the leading manufacturers and suppliers of telecommunications equipment. In 1978 it established itself in the UK, with its headquarters in Risley, Warrington as a subsidiary of its Canadian parent company Gandalf. In September 1990, Gandalf (UK) became an independent commercial arm of Gandalf Digital Communications Ltd. (Canada). The company's main ISDN products consist of:

Starmaster - hardware & software system

This is an information network processor system that integrates PCs, Mainframes, LANs, WANs and ISDN, also containing gateways to X.25, Ethernet under TCP/IP and SNA with IBM3270 (see Fig.14). The concept of this system in terms of inter-networking capabilities is simple to understand but its implementation is rather complex. It currently supports PRA, with BRA support due to be released November 1990. For PRA support Gandalf will introduce a PRM module. This provides connectivity to primary rate services, such as ISDN30. The PRM module will support a single primary rate ISDN link with common channel signalling in time slot 16. Compliance with a range of signalling protocols, such as DASS2 and ECMA106, facilitates connection to public and private ISDN services. This system interfaces with various proprietary switching equipment, for example Siemens MCX PABX, providing the usual management utilities expected from such a system.

TA-1 basic rate interface terminal adaptor

This was their first ISDN product, (released in the UK in August 1990). The TA-1 is a stand-alone unit that converts data to and from ISDN compatible data streams, connecting two local non-ISDN equipment ports (e.g. terminals, PCs, muxes or LANs) to the Basic Rate ISDN service. It allows up to two 56 or 64 Kbps synchronous channels to be connected from X.21/V35 interfaces to the I.420 basic rate 2B+D service. Typical applications for the TA-1 are file transfer between PCs and remote host and video conferencing, where the two B Channels are combined into a single 128 Kbps channel.

8900 Multi-source information display system

This is an integrated voice and data system allowing the sharing of database information. This system allows the user to window up to eight simultaneous sessions with access to eight different hosts (four synchronous and four asynchronous).

Line miser dov 640 - data over voice multiplexing equipment

This system consists of a data switch combined with data-over-voice multiplexing equipment and connections to existing telephone and terminal equipment. It is based upon digital technology providing 64Kbps synchronous transmissions on existing two-wire telephone lines.

MUX 2000 system - multiplexer

This multiplexer provides voice/data transport, statistical and time division multiplexing, X.25 packet switching transport, D-channel capability and B channel capacity over a 64Kbps link.

According to Mr. David Langley, Manager European Technology Centre at Risley, Gandalf's marketing strategy for its ISDN product range is aimed at supplying the ISDN communications market with the necessary hardware so as to build inter-networking applications, linking existing hardware to the new technology. Some of the applications Langley sees as being of fundamental importance for their products are:

- Starmaster as a WAN integrator (see Fig.14)

- Local Access through Starmaster to an ISDN compatible PABX or Host. In this area, Gandalf have already developed an interface with Siemens MCX PBX and have a Memorandum of Understanding with other PBX manufacturers, including GPT, Alcatel, AT&T and Northern Telecom to have an interface between these PBXs by 1993

- Through the development of a smaller version of their Starmaster system, called Access Server, the provision of a multi-service Primary Rate Multiplexer, (see Fig.15)

Further development within the ISDN communications environment is envisaged by Langley in terms of an ISDN PC card, which will work as a gateway for LANs into ISDN. This product is expected to be released towards the end of the first quarter of 1991. An ISDN workstation product is also under investigation, but no dates were given for the release of this product.

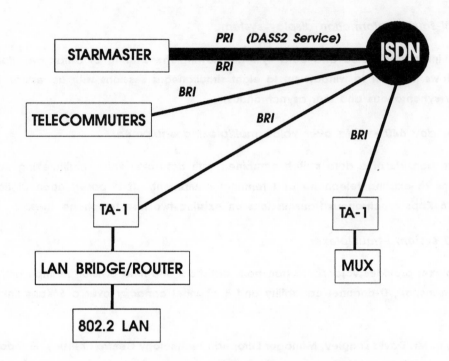

Figure 14   WAN Integrator

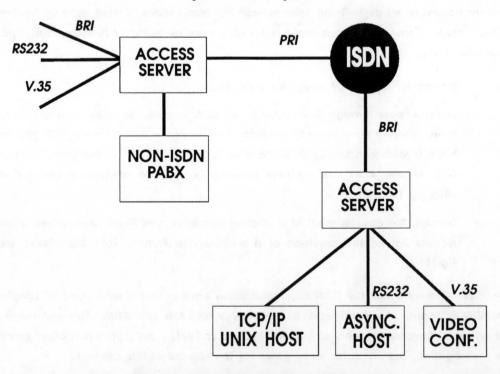

Figure 15   Multiservice Primary Rate Multiplexer

Digital Equipment Co. Ltd (DEC)

DEC have been offering a voice and data integrated system linking their VAX machines to a Public or Private PBX since 1988. This product is called Computer Integrated Telephony (CIT)(see Fig.16).

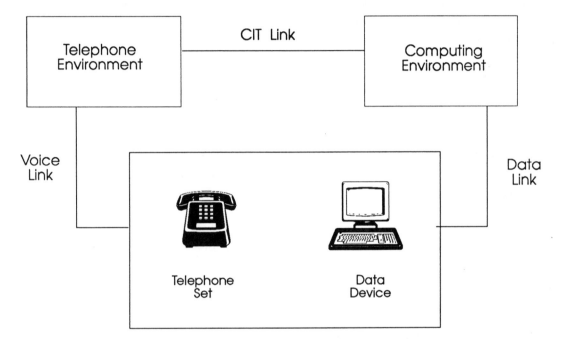

Integrated Desk

Figure 16   CIT

CIT is the functional integration of end-user applications with the telephone. The application works by providing a physical connection between a PBX and a computer system, then using the link to pass PBX requests and status information between the two, so that the application running on the computer can use the status information and can control the requests issued.

CIT is made up of two software components:

CIT Application Interface (CITAI)

This component facilitates the interface between a PBX and the application in an "open" environment, i.e. it is not dependent on PBX characteristics and protocols. Hence it allows the user's application to be easily transferred to other exchanges. This interface needs to be installed on every VAX within the LAN.

CIT PBX Server (CITSR)

The server VAX is connected to the PBX by a 9.6Kbps link. Each PBX to be utilized must be linked to its unique VAX running the server software, but can be accessed by applications running on other VAXes on the LAN.

The PBXs that directly support (via an interface) this system presently are:

- BT Regent Generic 257

- Northern Telecom Meridian SL-1

- Siemens Hicom 340-370 & 390

- Mitel SX-2000

with the following companies supporting Digital's CIT in an "open system environment":

- Ericsson Telephone Company

- NEC

- Philips Telecommunications & Data Systems

- Plessey Business Systems

CIT has attracted some interest from several organisations, who have developed third party applications based on this system. The following are the three best known third party applications:

Telemanager by Enator Ltd

This is a software product residing on a MicroVAX, and providing additional call management and distribution functions to a standard PABX. It provides some basic functions such as call routeing and queueing, fast answering and performance monitoring, in addition to re-allocation of trunk and agent groups, re-configuration of PABX/ACD (Automatic call distribution) functions and integration of ACD operations and computer applications

FOCUS/CIT Interface by Information Builders (UK) Ltd

The FOCUS/CIT software interface allows users to develop VAX-based applications with this 4GL/DBMS tool integrating CIT characteristics. It provides for the integration of simultaneous data and voice transmission based on database information, application logic and telephone extension availability.

TBS Link from British Telecom

The Telemarketing Business System (TBS) combines the capabilities of a VAX/VMS computer with BT's TBS application software. This software based system includes facilities for screen presentation layout, database management, customer account management, auto-dialling, customised reporting and performance management. This link provides a digital interface between the computer, the telephone and the PBX/ACD and can instruct and question the PBX/ACD.

Other DEC ISDN Products

DEC have released the DEC ISDN 2B+D Mini-computer Communications Controller 100 (DIV32) with associated software in France, Germany and USA, and will be released in the UK late October/early November 1990. Furthermore it intends to support Australia and Japan in the near future. This product provides DEC systems with Basic Rate Access to ISDN.

HARDWARE: The *DEC ISDN Controller 100* is a single board, synchronous communications controller providing ISDN BRA that can be fitted directly into a Q-bus MicroVAX system box. This can be a stand-alone system or function in a LAN as an Ethernet Server, providing ISDN connectivity for Non-Q-bus systems. Each hardware module supports one ISDN BRA line, with support for text, data and image, but it does not support voice.

SOFTWARE: The *VAX ISDN Software* is loaded into the Q-bus VAX host to control the ISDN connection. In addition VAX ISDN ACCESS software is available to enhance ISDN management.

This software controls the ISDN signalling channel (D) and therefore controls the connecti using the two bearer channels (B). As each B channel is independently managed, two different protocols can be simultaneously run on both channels.

With the existing capabilities of the DEC VAX mini-computer, ISDN BRA and the DEC ISDN Controller 100, it is envisaged that the following applications could be developed:

- Consultation of images databases
- High definition facsimile
- Graphic mail messaging
- Order entry, processing and inquiry
- Automatic Number Identification for scanning databases
- Message Desk Services

DEC's marketing strategy for ISDN revolves around their mini-computers and the use of these in an inter-networking environment. According to Phil Barton, Telephony Marketing Manager, "the 2B+D products can be used with most of our mini-computers (micro VAXes) to enable them to communicate over a Wide Area Network, with either DECnet or X.25 communications protocols". In this environment, DEC believe that ISDN is an alternative Wide Area Networking service, complementing existing leased lines (e.g. BT's Kilostream) and Public Packet Switched Networks.

DEC's future involvement in ISDN products will depend greatly on international business plans that demonstrate a reasonable rate of return, and will also be affected by the availability of ISDN lines from BT and Mercury within the UK. Barton explains that their strategy is dependent on BT's strategy, noting that "If BT gets the tariffs right, then ISDN could take off, alternatively it will flop".

5 Case studies

ICI - corporate management services

ICI is the third largest industrial company in the UK and twentieth in the European Community, with a turnover of £4 to £5 billion per year. ICI is split up into 12 divisions each operating independently of each other but dependent on the Corporate Management Services for IT research and support. Their existing telecommunications environment consists of 60 PABXs in the UK, a worldwide private packet switching system running over 64 Kbits leased lines, a worldwide SNA network supporting IBM mainframes, and a worldwide DECNET network supporting over 100 DEC machines.

According to Mr. A. Richardson (Telecoms and Workstation Development Group - ICI Corporate Management Services) ICI currently have several Pilot ISDN projects, each one initiated by user demand for better quality decision support and research tools. Furthermore every project is being studied independently of the others, depending on where the need is. This begs the question of whether ICI had a corporate IT strategy on ISDN. Richardson said "There is no company wide strategy in ICI for ISDN; ICI's autonomous divisions decide independently of each other whether to use one tool or another. The user is our (Corporate Management Services) client and he decides whether we should be spending money on one product or another" . Obviously if the trend continues towards using this technology it is safe to assume that eventually ICI must include ISDN into their Corporate IT Strategy.

The projects that Mr. Richardson mentioned were as follows:

Group 4 facsimile application

In collaboration with the British Lending Library (BLL) in London, ICI use this tool for research purposes. Requests for information in the form of scientific photographs/documents/graphs/pictures are sent to the BLL who transmit the required documents back to ICI. This application is now running in two Divisions (Chemicals and Polymers & Pharmaceutical) and also in the UK and USA HQ.

Future development using this tool will consist of integrating this to an online Database and E-Mail. This application was justified in terms of time saved. Previously it would take at least five days for such a request to be executed while now it takes, on average, four hours.

Private video conferencing

This system is based on 2Mb links using either the GPT/BT system or PictureTel. It mainly connects adjacent sites, although a trial system is being tested between USA and Australia.

ICL DRS ISDN intelligent workstation

At the moment ICI are investigating the use of this workstation for their information analysts to help them gather information at a much quicker rate.

Videophones

Videophones have been installed on the Senior Executives and Directors' desks, as this technology is seen as enhancing the executives' management role and helping in their day-to-day business activity.

Midland bank plc

Midland Bank is ranked the third largest bank amongst the UK clearing houses, with a turnover of £405 million p.a.

Midland's existing telecommunications environment consists of an internal Value Added Network Service employing a structured cabling system based on the use of optical fibre, which is their primary transport medium for data traffic and includes a private X.25 communications service. They utilise Timeplex Link1 to manage the bandwidth and for point-to-point data services. This is also used as a transport mechanism for external X.25 services. Midland's internal voice network includes PSTN breakout facility for analogue and digital transmissions. They are currently utilising BT's ISDN 30 service as a cost effective file transfer mechanism and backup service.

According to Mr. J. Donald, (Voice Services Group - Midland Group Telecoms Services), ISDN could be of great utility to the group in several areas, namely:

- In terms of an internal private ISDN network, it could be the vehicle for internal video conferencing.

- The use of ISDN as the medium for fast file transfer to branches. This could be used to distribute video training courses or monthly accounts.

- ISDN could be used as a dial-up Kilostream backup at 64kbps.

- The use of Calling Line Identity would be of advantage to the management of corporate accounts.

- The use of the "D" low bit rate channel as an "authorization transport mechanism" for credit card services.

6 Broadband ISDN - the future

So far we have considered a revolution in communications and cost and time saving applications, but the real revolution will only occur when the speed, quality and volume of transmission is multiplied by a factor of at least 100. This could mean that applications that required speed, quality and volume might be developed.

At present, narrowband ISDN facilitates the integration of the telecommunications networks in terms of data, telephony and video communications, but for higher quality, speed and volume the capacity required is not presently available. Hence many future users of ISDN will be waiting impatiently for a full implementation of B-ISDN (Broadband ISDN).

Before we discuss the significance of B-ISDN, what is meant by bandwidth in terms of ISDN? Many users have great difficulty in understanding this concept. For example, if we wish to transmit the equivalent pages of text as contained in a box of paper, containing 2500 A4 sheets, which could weigh about 16Kg, from A to B we could have used the following two systems:

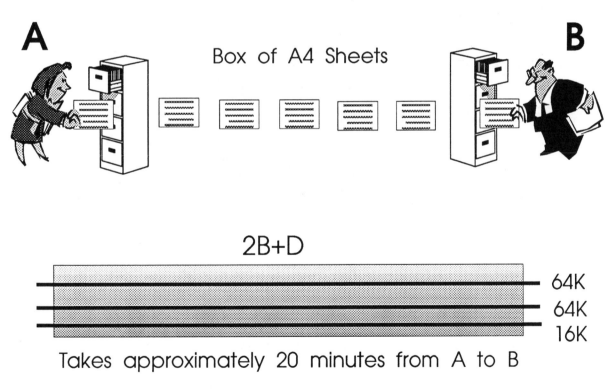

Figure 17 Transmission of a box of typed paper from A to B

In Fig.17, using the 2B+D Service with two channels of 64K, the transmission would take approximately 20 minutes to reach its destination. In Fig.18, using the 30B+D Service with 30 64K channels (e.g. 2Mbps), the transmission would only take approximately 40 seconds to reach its destination. The times and figures used in Figures 17 and 18 are given as guides to explain the differences between bandwidths, and hence are not exact, furthermore it is assumed that the 64K channels are used concurrently.

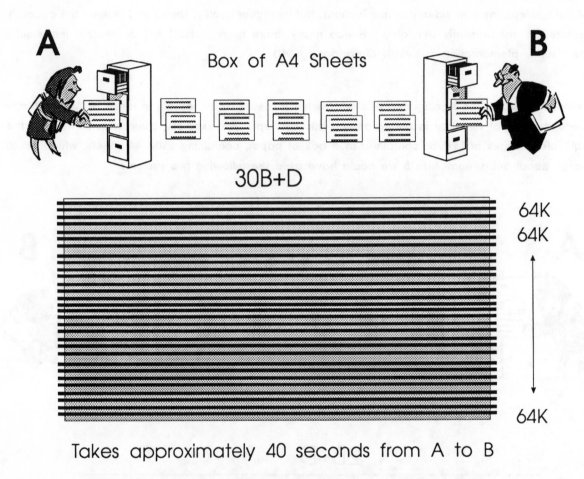

Figure 18 Transmission of the same box of paper at a higher rate

Therefore, with broadband ISDN, it will be possible to transmit a boxful of paper at the blink of an eyelid? B-ISDN will enable users to push more data through larger "pipelines" at faster speeds, but speed is just one aspect of the benefits of B-ISDN. Let's now look at how B-ISDN is defined and how it could be used.

B-ISDN is visualised as being an all-purpose digital network that will use high-capacity fibre optic technology. Furthermore, the network should support both switched and non-switched connections, and provide integrated services features, maintenance and network management functions.

The channel support rate definition described in the CCITT Blue Book (i.e. the CCITT Blue Book is the 1988 set of telecommunications recommendations) is as follows (with the first five channels already defined for narrowband ISDN and the last three for B-ISDN):

CHANNEL	SPEED	APPLICATION
B	64 Kbit/s	Encoded Voice
D	64 Kbit/s	Signalling
H_0	384 Kbit/s	Slow Speed Video
H_{11}	1.5 Mbit/s	Motion Video
H_{12}	1.9 Mbit/s	Motion Video
H_{21}	32 Mbit/s	Undefined
H_{22}	43-45 Mbit/s	Undefined
H_4	132-138 Mbit/s	Undefined
Where: $4 \times H_{21}$ rate $<= H_4$ rate $3 \times H_{22}$ rate $<= H_4$ rate		

Note: Information taken from the CCITT Blue Book, Vol. III, Fascicle III.7 and Fascicle III.8, ISDN recommendation I.121 & I.412

The transfer mode (more commonly known as the transport mechanism) chosen by the CCITT Study Group XVIII Task Group is Asynchronous Transfer Mode (ATM). ATM is a high-bandwidth, low-delay, packet-like switching and multiplexing technique which deals with the rules for dividing up the available bandwidth on an interface and allocation to user services. A channel associates a portion of the bandwidth with a service; this bandwidth is then segmented into fixed-size information-carrying simple frames or cells, each cell containing a header and information field. These cells can be allocated to services on demand and are used in both circuit and packet modes, the latter being processed and switched at exceedingly high speeds.

Bearing in mind the definition of B-ISDN and the probability of greater technological advance in the future, we can now consider at the potential services that B-ISDN could facilitate:

High speed communications and retrieval of data, documents, hi-fi sound, still images, text and graphics. The applications covered by these services could be:

- Computer aided design and manufacturing (CAD/CAM)
- Electronic picture editing
- News retrieval
- Program downloading
- Tele-shopping and advertisement
- Document retrieval from information centres
- High resolution image library
- High speed facsimile

Person-to-Person video communication and messaging

- High resolution and quality video telephony
- Video mail, including store-and-forward, mailbox and message handling functions

Access to video information

- Broadband videotex, which will include sound, images in TV standards and short film scenes in addition to current text and graphics

- Electronic mail-order catalogue plus ordering services

- Travel brochure plus ordering service

- Pay television

- High Definition Television (HDTV)

7 ISDN - management and migration issues

Most ISDN marketing gurus would have us believe that ISDN is the perfect solution to all problems. It is probably true to say that ISDN will *initially* only provide some new capabilities and features as about 90% of the services offered by ISDN are already being provided by other means.

Analogue telecommunications services are currently the norm although these are slowly being replaced by an integrated digital network comprising of digital transmission, digital switching and distributed computing. With this in mind, any organisation considering the utilization of ISDN must plan the migration thoroughly. The reasons for planning for ISDN are fairly simple:

- To recognise the most beneficial utilisation of ISDN's variety of services and options

- Current networks are large and complex; any change needs to be considered in terms of cost and disruption

- Being a 'pioneer' in the use of ISDN brings with it many fears, risks and uncertainty, although the rewards can be substantial.

The problems of migration are specific to each organisation and the issue needs to be incorporated into the strategic business plan over a reasonable length of time, e.g. a minimum of five years.

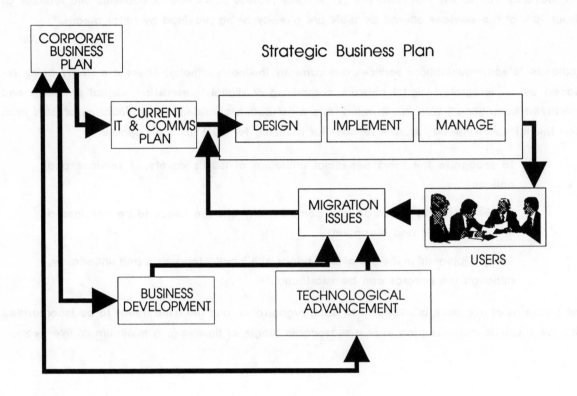

Figure 19 Migration Issues

The Planning Model presented in Fig.19 describes the typical cycle that an organisation will undertake when evaluating and implementing any new technology. As you will see from the diagram, a long-term coherent plan should cover every aspect of the decision making and implementation process, from user requirements to organisational and budgetary constraints.

The introduction of a migration plan often starts with a corporate business plan that can be influenced by the changing business and technological environments, leading to a "predicted IT and communications Plan" (which tries to identify what the short term needs in this area will be) and finally to the short term implementation cycle.

This process may be reiterated many times, where migration issues will influence future expectations.

By considering the migration issues box and the short-term implementation cycle illustrated in   Fig. 19, we can construct a Study Plan that will help us in evaluating ISDN.

The following specimen Study Plan is structured so as to identify the risks and benefits associated with the introduction of new technology. It is not intended to be a definite set of planning instructions, but may be a useful guide.

ISDN study plan

1 Investigate existing services and objectives

Summarise the current voice, data and integrated voice/data networks you may have, include any usage of Value Added Data Services (VADs). Once you have a good understanding of the existing services then investigate your organisation's overall requirements and objectives, specifically the issue of integrated services, as this is obviously one of ISDN's cost-saving advantages.

In terms of cost savings remember to consider both the short and long term effects. In the short term, it is likely that cost savings will be marginal, as most existing services will continue to be used. In the long term, ISDN is expected to provide greater cost effectiveness and customer control as it becomes universally available.   (For example, modems will no longer be needed, as the service will be digital).

2 Ask the right questions

Take time and care to formulate a comprehensive list of questions that need answers before a decision on whether or not to use ISDN can be made. For example:

Business Questions
How could your business change if you had access to high speed, high quality digital circuits to all your locations?

What is the potential user base within your company?

This study should identify the workgroups that could potentially use ISDN; these workgroups could be split up as follows:

- by geographic separation
- those users that are using PCs & Fax to share information and images
- those users that are sharing information from information servers
- those users that spend over 50% of their time travelling to attend meetings.

How will ISDN impact your users?

The translation of the expected benefits of ISDN into their impact on your users will enable an intelligent evaluation of the potential use of ISDN.

What about connections to your customers and clients?

Who will be providing which ISDN services, where, when and for what price?

How many "trunk lines" could you eliminate?

Although this question may sound technical, its purpose is to identify if any economies of scale exist. Digital trunks are more cost effective than analogue ones, and with ISDN PRA, 30 simultaneous connections can be supported on one digital trunk group.

Who will manage the connection to ISDN services within the organisation?

This is a business issue because the cost of training for new technology can be high in terms of both time and money.

Who will be interworking ISDN services with the existing telephone and data networks, where, when and for what price?

What are the current and future plans of the suppliers of ISDN products?

Will the supplier upgrade existing products to the characteristics required in the future?

Who will be keeping your senior executives educated and informed?

In any high risk costly evaluation, Senior Management must be made aware of all the resulting benefits and drawbacks. After a complete evaluation of the services, you will be unlikely to conclude that ISDN has no place in your organisation's networking strategy, your organisation must know about it, be able to explain it, evaluate it's impact on your business, etc.

Technical ISDN Questions

What is ISDN?

Develop an understanding of ISDN, specifically the unique capabilities likely to become available.

Can ISDN resolve your peak-load problems?

For example, in times of peak load by utilising the calling line identity feature of ISDN you will not only know who is calling, but you could capture this information and call them back.

What do ISDN line interfaces do to your PBXs?

Which ISDN standards, options and inter-networking does the products you are investigating comply with?

An Open System strategy will be advantageous.

Will the equipment and software work?

This is an all encompassing question containing a number of other questions like:

- To which ISDN standards and options does the vendor's services, equipment and software conform?

- What quarantees does the user have that the product completely conforms to standards and not to ambiguous advertising claims?

- Will it work with my systems and applications?

- How will it interface with all my existing hardware, i.e. PCs, Networks, Mainframe etc.?

- Ask for a reference from existing users? When talking to an existing user try to get as much information as possible on the products and supplier. His experiences, good or bad are essential to your evaluation process. Remember that if he (the user) has made a major mistake he will probably not want to talk about it, hence your questions have to be both probing and sympathetic.

How can any existing terminal and computer equipment be upgraded to ISDN?

Who is providing ISDN network products and services?

What are the costs (tariff plus CPE enhancement) versus benefits?

Furthermore, a testing strategy needs to be devised before making a decision to go ahead. If field testing is not possible then you will have to consider whether you can rely on what ever conformance testing the vendor may have performed.

An ISDN conformance certificate (or "seal of approval") issued by the British Approvals Board in Telecommunications (BABT) and conforming to the European Telecommunications Standards Institute (ETSI) ISDN specification while it probably will not guarantee that the product is fully compatible with others, but it does imply that the manufacturer has made a commitment to ISDN and that he has the knowledge required to support ISDN.

3 Identify and prioritise application areas

In the search for innovative applications it is important not to lose sight of the final objectives, those being to have the right applications for your company. In order to do this you must be both a dreamer and a realist. A dreamer because you are going to need all your imagination in trying to find the right innovative application and a realist so that you do not lose sight of your organisation's final goal, to have that elusive competitive edge.

It is impossible to investigate all the possible ISDN applications, so try to identify those applications that have a high payoff and fast response. Considering the following questions may assist the recognition of those applications which show early return on investment:

- Can the organisation benefit from faster response times?

- Can the users benefit from the increased integration of the data and telecommunications functions?

- Does the organisation use multiple sets of access lines for different telecommunications services, e.g. facsimile and telex?

- Do you need multi-purpose terminals in order to integrate the services required?

- Does the application require the transmission of high volumes of data?

- Could your organisation's users and business colleagues benefit from exchanging pictures, documents or files during a telephone conversation?

An example of how an investigation could be structured is illustrated below:

PRIORITY LEVEL	TECHNOLOGY USED	FUNCTION	EXPECTED BENEFIT
1	Group 4 Fax VideoConferencing	Document Management Project Management	Reduce Cost Increase Quality
2	Call Manager Screen Sharing	Professional Worker Administrative Worker	Personal Productivity
3	Remote Access	Telecommuting	Flexibility to cope with changed competitive circumstances Reduction in travel & decrease in skills shortage

4 User qualification study

An investigation into what the user is currently utilising and present costs associated with the user's work practices would be useful in a study of Point 6. Some of the questions to be considered are:

- What is the existing IT equipment base?
- How much demand is placed on the voice network?
- What use is made of facsimile, telex, electronic mail, couriers?
- Are there offices in varying geographic locations?
- Is there a large travel associated cost?
- Are there sufficient management controls if remote working exists?
- What is the percentage of skilled workers?

5 Integrate network management

This means integrating voice and data network management, video networks, security networks, building controls, etc. Hence the responsibility of ISDN network management becomes a joint task for those responsible for voice and data communications. This implies that the personnel responsible must have cross-training and knowledge in both areas.

6 Build a cost model

The cost categories considered will depend on the specific situation and the way ISDN fits into the organisation's objectives and plans. Taking into account the possible benefits of ISDN, such as faster data rates, can lead to the identification of areas where costs can be eliminated or reduced, for example, equipment, cabling, services, salaries, etc. Below is a table that describes some of the areas where costs need to be investigated.

AREA	INCREASE/DECREASE COSTS	ELIMINATE COSTS
Wiring		
NT Equipment		
Telephone sets		
Training		
Service		
Management time		
Consulting fees		
Capital cost of equipment		
Cost of space		
Cost of training		
Running costs		

7 Procurement and implementation

Once the process of identifying the impact ISDN may have on your organisation has been completed, which involves defining ISDN's functionality, technology, costs, ease of use, reliability and performance, you are then in a position to define your next steps.

The development of a corporate wide strategy with the commitment of your Senior Executives must be your first step. This strategy should identify the objectives of the project and how they can be achieved, who is going to be responsible for the implementation and how its implementation is going to be resourced.

The phases that may be followed in this procurement and implementation stage could be as follows:

Phase 1	Formally analyse the full operational requirements.
Phase 2	Cross check requirements with objectives and users.
Phase 3	Write a clear and unambiguous specification.
Phase 4	Develop a Pilot Project, identifying all your needs, for example, training requirements.
Phase 5	Identify your suppliers.
Phase 6	Send out your invitation to tender for your pilot project to your prospective suppliers.
hase 7	Liaise with your supplier, facilitating them with the necessary information they need to give you a complete picture of what they can offer.
Phase 8	Select your supplier(s) and equipment.
Phase 9	Negotiate a Memorandum of Agreement, where you commit to use the supplier's equipment after the successful pilot period.
Phase 10	Run the Pilot and conduct tests. These tests should be based upon an agreed programme (i.e. agreed with your users, implementation team and the supplier) and test standards.

Phase 11   If the Pilot is successful, negotiate a contract with your existing supplier or identify new suppliers. If a new supplier is required, follow steps 5 to 9 again.

Phase 12   **Develop a final implementation roll-out.**

Phase 13   **Training of users.**

Phase 14   **Negotiate a maintenance agreement.**

8 1992 – the likely evolution of ISDN implementation

By the end of 1992 Europe will open its national barriers to people, goods and capital. This is the idea behind the 1985 Single Act, which not only legislates for the inauguration of the Single Market by 1993 but establishes a framework for an economic and social territory.

This milestone in the creation of the European Market Place will markedly increase the requirement for an efficient European telecommunications infrastructure.

The European Commission (EC) has set itself some vital goals in the establishment of a Pan-European telecommunications network:

- The creation of community-wide network integrity.

- The creation of community-wide services and standards.

- An Open Common Market for telecommunications.

- A European market for telecommunications terminals.

ISDN could play a major role in accomplishing these goals, and to this aim a Memorandum of Understanding (MoU) was agreed and signed between the European Network Operators (e.g. British Telecom, Mercury, France Telecom, Deutsche Bundespost, Telefónica, etc.) to enable Pan-European ISDN services to be offered across Europe by 1992.

But how will all this hype and ISDN Euro-awareness affect the end user?

To consider this problem, it is necessary to distinguish between the small and large organisations, as each will have a different requirement for ISDN, especially with regard to the amount transmitted via an ISDN link.

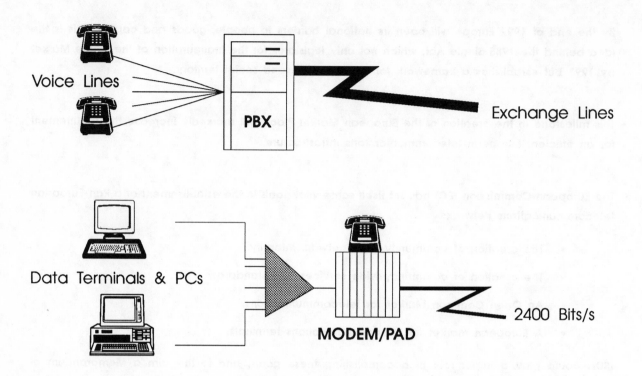

Voice Lines

PBX

Exchange Lines

Data Terminals & PCs

MODEM/PAD

2400 Bits/s

Small Organisation Today

Figure 20

Figure 20 shows the typical telecommunications structure of the small organisation today. It relies on the PSTN for its voice requirements and uses dial-up modems for its data transmission. In the present ISDN market the initial investment made by small private companies could be large due to having to acquire either ISDN terminals or terminal adapters.

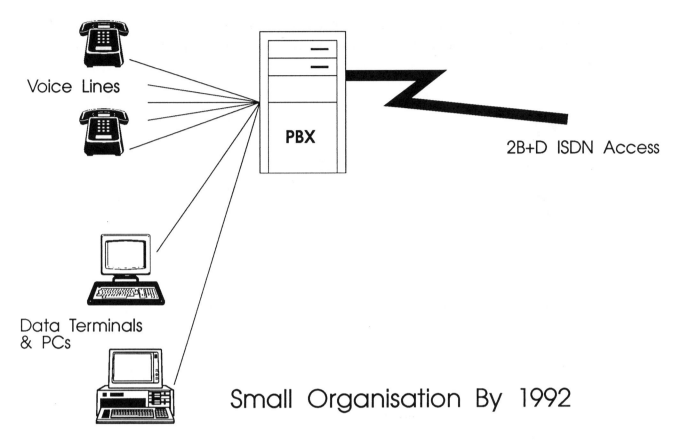

Voice Lines

PBX

2B+D ISDN Access

Data Terminals
& PCs

Small Organisation By 1992

Figure 21

By 1992 (as shown in Fig.21) the situation should have changed, allowing it to use Basic Access ISDN, which will give it at least 25 times current speeds at the same calling cost as placing a normal voice call.

If we now look at a large organisation, assuming that it is a multi-sited company, each site having voice and data communications requirements, then the company will probably have its own private data network (see Fig.22).

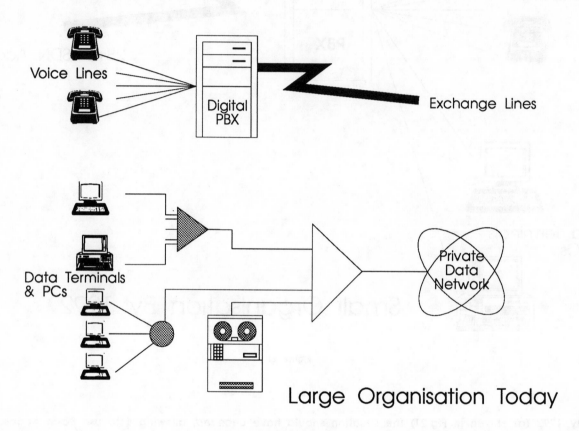

Large Organisation Today

Figure 22

By the end of 1992, this large organisation will probably have access to 30B+D services with its own ISDN PBX. Interconnection between the voice and data networks will also be available by then (see Fig.23).

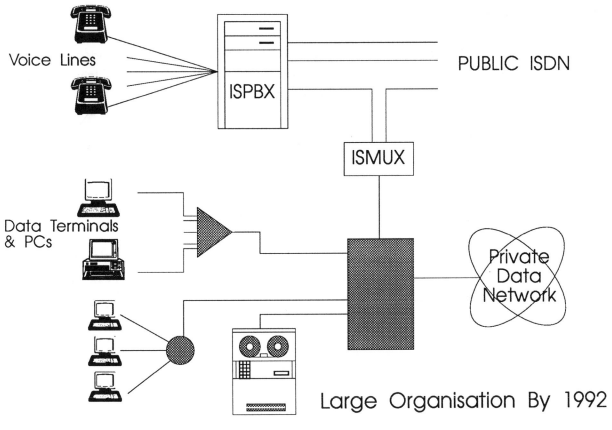

Figure 23

Of all the changes that will take place over the next few years, the implementation of ISDN will be a major event in the world of telecommunications. This will transform the working practices of organisations large and small, but most significantly ISDN will drastically change the smaller companies' use of telecommunications.

Many countries have already successfully completed ISDN trials and have pilot services in their main cities. The main consequence of ISDN deployment is that the transition from analogue telephony to integrated digital services is no longer a concept of the future but a reality.

Conclusion

In Europe the implementation of a Pan-European telecommunications service is being taken very seriously. The RACE project (Research and Development for Advance Communications in Europe), run by the DG-XIII of the European Commission has as its objective the "Introduction of Integrated Broadband Communications taking into account the evolving ISDN and national introduction strategies, progressing to Community-wide services by 1995". This project has as its main goal the setting up of an ideal, inexpensive telecommunications network based on B-ISDN, where an ideal telecommunications network should support every imaginable service by transporting and switching signals, at the minimum possible cost, from any terminal equipment connected to it.

With the introduction of Pan-European narrowband ISDN services, B-ISDN will become possible in the foreseeable future, as a relatively small amount of development work is required to enhance the European connections. This work will ensure that ISDN will become a worldwide all-purpose communications tool.

Basic ISDN will change the working practices of the smaller companies radically, but B-ISDN is what the major multinational companies will invest in, as B-ISDN will supply them with the speed and volume they require for inter-company communications.

Glossary of terms

A and B Signalling
: A type of in-band signalling used in T1 transmission in which certain bits in the data channels are used for signalling purposes.

A-channel
: The standard telephone channel which carries analogue voice signals over the nominal frequency range of 300-3400 Hz.

A-Law
: A European logarithmic encoding algorithm used for converting analogue voice signals to digital signals. The A-Law is incompatible with the American Mu-Law.

Analogue Transmission
: Transmission of a continuously variable signal (the usual transmission method for telephone signals) as opposed to a discretely variable signal (digital transmission).

API
: *Application Programming Interface*

Asynchronous Transmission
: A transmission technique in which each information character is individually synchronised using start and stop elements (or bits).

ATDM
: *Asynchronous Time Division Multiplexing.* A technique which time division multiplexes asynchronous signals by oversampling.

ATM
: *Asynchronous Transfer Mode.* The transport mechanism for all data and other information on a broadband ISDN.

B-channel
: A bearer or information channel in an ISDN which provides a throughput of 64 Kbps.

B-ISDN
: *Broadband ISDN*

BABT	*British Approvals Board for Telecommunications.* The approvals body for apparatus connecting to public networks, formed under the provision of the Telecommunications Act (1984).
Bandwidth	The range of frequencies that can pass over a given circuit under given conditions of signal loss or distortion; measured in Hz.
Baseband Signal	A raw unmodulated signal operating at the base of the bandwidth (0-48 KHz) which is encoded directly onto the transmission medium.
Bearer Service	A type of service provided by an ISDN that provides the ability to transmit data signals between users.
Bis	Literally means "the second part"; used in CCITT Recommendations to indicate a variation of an original CCITT Recommendation.
Bps **(Bits per second)**	A measure of the rate of information transfer over a data channel.
BRA	*Basic Rate Access.* An ISDN interface structure providing a 144 Kbps data rate broken down into two 64 Kbps B-channels and one 16 Kbps signalling channel (D-channel).
Breakout Box	A device that allows access to individual points on a physical interface connector for testing and monitoring.
Broadband	Refers to communications using a bandwidth which is broader than that used for voice communications (also known as wideband).

Broadband Data Channel	A channel which has a wider bandwidth than a voice grade channel and can provide a number of channels simultaneously.
BT	*British Telecommunications.* One of the British PTTs, formerly known as Post Office Telecommunications, and usually referred to as British Telecom.
CATV	*Community Antenna Television.* The distribution of television signals from a central point by means of cables (also known as Cable Television).
CAD/CAM	*Computer Aided Design/Computer Aided Manufacturing.* A method of production employing designs provided by a computer aided design (CAD) system.
CBX	*Computerised Branch Exchange.* A local network based on the digital private branch exchange architecture which provides an integrated voice/data switching service.
CCITT	*Consultative Committee for International Telephony and Telegraphy.* An advisory committee established under the United Nations, within the ITU to recommend worldwide standards for telecommunications.
CCITT Signalling System No. 7	A common channel signalling system recommended by the CCITT for signalling in an ISDN.
CCS	*Common Channel Signalling.* A system of signalling between exchanges on a data network in which call control signals (and management signals) relating to a number of channels are conveyed over a single channel by addressed messages.

CCTV	*Closed Circuit Television.* **One of the many services found on broadband networks and often used for surveillance.**
Centrex Central Exchange.	**A service which provides a number of customers with most of the facilities of a PBX from a central public exchange; a number of logical (virtual) PBXs provided from a central exchange.**
CEPT	*Conference of European Postal and Telecommunications Administrations.* **An organisation whose aim is to establish closer relationships between European PTTs, provide a common European stance for input to CCITT and to provide a European standard on CCITT Recommendations where options exist.**
Channel	**A logical information path capable of transmitting data in one or two directions. Generally a number of logical channels are carried over a single physical circuit (such as a cable, or radio waves).**
Channel Speed	**The speed or rate at which data flows through a channel.**
CIT	*Computer Integrated Telephony*
CLI	*Calling Line Identity*
Codec	*Coder/Decoder.* **A device which combines the coding (from analogue to digital) and decoding (digital to analogue) of a signal.**
Common Carrier	**A term used to describe a tele-communications network provider.**

Communications Architecture	The hardware and software structure that implements communication functions.
Communications Network	A collection of interconnected functional units that provides a data communications service among stations attached to the network.
Compression	The application of any of several techniques that reduce the number of bits required to represent information in data transmission (or storage), thus conserving bandwidth (or memory).
CPE	*Customer Premises Equipment*
CSMA/CD	*Carrier Sense Multiple Access / Collision Detect.* A medium access control method for a multiple access transmission media in which a terminal wishing to transmit first listens to the medium and only transmits if the medium is idle. It ceases transmission if it detects a collision.
D-channel	A data channel primarily intended for carrying signalling and control data over an ISDN circuit between the network and an ISDN terminal.
DASS2	*Digital Access Signalling System No. 2.* DASS2 provides common channel signalling between a digital PBX and a local SPC exchange. Specified by BT to provide multiple ISDN connections.
Data Over Voice	An FDM technique which combines voice and data on the same circuit by assigning a portion of the unused bandwidth to data.

Data PBX	A PBX used solely for data and which is distinguished from a PBX in that only digital, and not analogue, transmission is supported.
DCE	*Data Circuit-terminating Equipment.* A device, either integrated with or separate from a terminal, that provides signal conversion and coding between a DTE and a circuit.
DECnet	The trademark for DEC's communications network architecture that permits interconnection of DEC computers using DDCMP.
Digital	Referring to a signalling technique in which data is transmitted by generating pulses of electromagnetic energy in a discontinuous (i.e. on/off) coded pattern representing bits in a data stream.
Digital Switching	The process of establishing and maintaining a connection, under stored program control, where binary coded information is routed between two end points.
Digital Telephone	An electronic telephone set that includes a Codec, so that all communication between the telephone and an exchange is in digital form.
Digital Transmission	A form of transmission in which data characters are coded into separate pulses of signal levels, whose various states are discrete intervals apart.
Digitisation	The conversion of analogue signals to a digital form which can then be stored or transmitted by a terminal.
DIP	*Document Image Processing*

DMI	*Digital Multiplexed Interface.* A voice/data PBX standard supported by AT&T for using T1 transmission involving 64 Kbps channels.
DNA	*Digital Network Architecture.* The network architecture developed by DEC.
DPNSS	*Digital Private Network Signalling System.* A system which provides common channel inter-PABX signalling via a 2 Mbps digital circuit.
Drop Cable	A flexible cable (twisted pair, coaxial, etc.) used to connect a user device to a main network trunk.
DTE	Data Terminal Equipment. A generic name for any user device connected to a data network, e.g. visual display unit, computer or office workstation etc.
E-series Recommendations	The set of CCITT recommendations for telephone networks and ISDN.
EDI	Electronic Data Interchange. The transfer of structured data, by agreed message standards, from one computer system to another, by electronic means.
Electronic Mail	Messages which are sent electronically between subscribers via a public or private communications system.
Ethernet	A low-level, contention bus, baseband LAN developed by Xerox Corporation and supported by Intel, DEC, and Hewlett-Packard.

ETSI	*European Telecommunications Standards Institute.* A body responsible for the development of European telecommunications standards; established as a non-affiliated standards body to take over standards making functions, primarily of CEPT.
Exchange	A switching centre in which telephone lines are interconnected.
Facsimile	A system for transmitting a copy of an image on a sheet of paper from one location to another over the telephone network or private circuit.
FDM	*Frequency Division Multiplexing.* A method by which the available transmission bandwidth is divided into narrower bands, each used for a separate channel.
FDMA	*Frequency Division Multiple Access.* A technique enabling communicating devices to share a multipoint or broadcast channel by allocating a different frequency to each user.
Fibre Optic	A glass-based transmission medium over which data is transmitted in the form of light waves or pulses. It is characterised by its potentially high bandwidth, high data carrying capability and its immunity to interference from electrical sources.
FOTS	*Fibre Optic Transmission System.* A system of multiple pairs of optical fibres in one cable, with appropriate terminating and amplifying equipment.
Framing	The process of inserting control bits to identify channels (used in TDM signals such as formatted T1).

Frequency	The rate of oscillation of a signal expressed in Hertz; Audio 30-3000 Hz; Radio 10+ kHz; VHF (very high frequency)30-300 MHz; UHF (ultra high frequency)300-3000 MHz.
Frequency Allocation	The band or block of frequencies in which specific types of users operate.
G-series Recommendations	The set of CCITT produced recommendations for digital networks, transmission systems and multiplexing equipments.
Gateway	A computer system or exchange in one network which allows access to and from another network; a system which interconnects different network architectures using different protocols by protocol translation.
H-channel	A high speed channel composed of a number of 64 Kbps B-channels in an ISDN.
HDLC	*High-level Data Link Control.* An ISO designed OSI data-link protocol for data transmission which does not use control characters and is data-independent.
HDTV	*High Definition Television*
Hz	*Hertz.* The measure of frequency equal to the number of cycles per second of a signal of varying voltage or current; one kHz (kilohertz) equals 10^3 Hz and one MHz (megahertz) equals 10^6 Hz.
I-series Recommendations	The set of recommendations produced by CCITT concerning ISDN. Refer to page 112.

ICBN   *Integrated Communications Broadband Network.* A generic reference to broadband ISDN.

IDA   *Integrated Digital Access.* The term for BT's Pilot ISDN services. These were available in two forms: Single Line IDA (BRA) and Multi Line IDA (PRA).   Now superceded by a fully commercial ISDN service.

IDN   *Integrated Digital Network.* A set of digital exchanges and links that uses integrated transmission and switching to provide digital connections between two or more points.

Integration   The bringing together of previously independent processes in a unified and coordinated manner.

Interface   The physical connection between two systems or devices; the definition of all signal characteristics and other specifications for physical interconnection of the devices.

ISDN   *Integrated Services Digital Network.* A communications network which uses digital transmission throughout to provide simultaneous handling of digitised voice and a variety of data traffic (such as Telex or Facsimile) on the same digital links and by the same digital exchanges.

ISPBX   *Integrated Services PBX.* A digital PBX which is used to terminate an ISDN and thus provide access to private ISDNs and direct access to public ISDNs.

IVDT   *Integrated Voice Data Terminal.* A device which features a terminal keyboard/display with varying degrees of local processing power and a voice telephone instrument; a device which can be used in conjunction with ISDN.

Jack	A term applied to a single-pin plug and its matching socket.
KiloStream	BT's digital leased line service offering point-to-point, kilobit per second telecommunications service.
LAN	*Local Area Network.* A general purpose local network which spans a limited geographical area (usually within one building or site) and interconnects a variety of computers, often at high data rate (1-50 Mbps).
LAPB	*Link Access Procedure, Balanced.* An packet-switched network link initialisation procedure which establishes and maintains communications between the DCE and DTE.
Leased Line	A line rented from a PTT exclusively to one customer for voice or data communications (also known as a private line, tie line or dedicated facility).
MAP	*Manufacturing Automation Protocol.* A token-passing bus LAN designed for factory environments by General Motors (similar to IEEE 802.4).
Mbps	*Megabits Per Second.* A measure of data rate in which 1 Megabit equals 1,048,576 bits (2^{20} bits).
MegaStream	BT's 2.048 Mbps digital,point-topoint, leased line telecommunications service.
Message	A complete transmission of data or text; a term sometimes used as a synonym for block.

Message Switching	A technique that transfers messages between points not directly connected by storing and forwarding them when facilities become available.
MODEM	*Modulator / Demodulator.* A DCE which converts digital serial data from a transmitting device into a form suitable for transmission over an analogue communications channel, e.g., a telephone line or private circuit.
Modulation	The application of information onto a carrier signal by varying one or more of the signal's characteristics (frequency, amplitude or phase); the conversion of a signal from its original digital format to analogue format.
Mu-Law	An American logarithmic encoding algorithm used for converting analogue voice signals to digital signals. The Mu-law is incompatible with the European A-Law.
Multiplex	To interleave or simultaneously transmit two or more messages on a single channel.
Multiplexer	A device that combines inputs from two or more devices and transmits the combined data stream over a single high speed channel.
Multipoint / Multidrop	A configuration in which more than two stations share a transmission path.
Network	A system of mutually communicating devices, such as computers, terminals or peripheral devices, connected in common and for a purpose by one or more transmission facilities.

Network Architecture	The philosophy and organisational concept for enabling communications between data processing equipment at multiple locations.
Network Management	A generic term used to embrace all the functions and entities involved in the management of a network (including configuration management, fault handling and the gathering of statistics relating to usage of the network).
NTE	*Network Terminating Equipment.* An ISDN term for an interface between an IDN and a subscriber which provides standard CCITT interfaces for the connection of DTEs.
NTSC	*National Television System Committee.* An American body that specified the NTSC colour TV in 1953.
OSCA	*Open Systems Cabling Architecture*
Open Architecture	The term used to described a system which has the ability to interconnect with systems from different suppliers.
PABX	*Private Automatic Branch Exchange.* A user-owned automatic telephone exchange; often used as a synonym of PBX.
Packet	A collection of bits that contains both control information (such as addressing, sequencing and error control) and user data.
Packet-Switching	A data communications technique in which data is transmitted by means of addressed packets and a transmission channel is occupied only for the duration of transmission of the packet; CCITT X.25 defines a wide-area packet-switching network.

PAD	*Packet Assembler/Disassembler.* An interface device which buffers data sent to and from character mode devices and then assembles and disassembles the packets needed for CCITT X.25 operation; an extension of CCITT X.25.
PAL	*Phase Alternation Line.* A system used in the UK, most of Europe, and elsewhere, for 625-line colour television signal transmission.
PBX	*Private Branch Exchange.* The controller of a user-owned telephone system, usually computer controlled.
PDN	*Public Data Network.* A communications system which is intended for transmission of digital data and is available to anyone who wishes to subscribe to it.
PRA	*Primary Rate Access.* An ISDN interface structure providing maximum data rates of 2.048 MHz in Europe and 1.544 MHz in America and Japan. The data rates are split into 64 Kbps PCM data channels, a 64 Kbps signalling channel and a 64 Kbps timing and synchronisation channel.
Prestel	A videotex service offered by BT.
PSDN	Packet-Switched Data Network. A generic title for a packet-switched network.
PSE	Packet-Switching Exchange. An exchange which enables the network to accept incoming packets and route them to the correct destination.

PSTN

Public Switched Telephone Network. The speech telephone network over which data calls may be made if there are modems at the receiving and transmitting ends of a communications link.

PTT

Postal, Telegraph and Telephone Authority. The name given to telecommunications administrations in Europe and elsewhere, which act as common carriers for telecommunications.

RACE

Research and Development into Advanced Communications in Europe. A European Community funded project which is researching and developing a European IBCN.

RJ-45

A miniature 8-wire plug and socket used in data communications (and in some ISDN variants).

RS-232C / RS-422 / RS-423

Standards laid down by the Electronics Institute Association (EIA) for interfacing digital devices to a modem. RS-232 is an interface standard for connecting a peripheral device to a computer.

SDLC

Synchronous Data Link Control. An IBM communications line protocol associated with SNA which allows efficient full duplex transmission.

SNA

Systems Network Architecture. The network architecture developed by IBM.

Switching

The process by which services or data are directed to the appropriate user across a communications network.

Synchronous	Having a constant time interval between successive bits, characters or events
Synchronous Data Channel	A communication channel capable of transmitting timing information, as well as data.
Synchronous Transmission	A transmission technique which uses no redundant information (such as start or stop bits) to identify the beginning of and end of characters, and thus is faster and more efficient than asynchronous transmission. Timing is done by using a clock to send synchronisation characters.
System X and Y	Digital SPC exchanges used by PTTs (System X is GPT manufactured, System Y is Ericsson manufactured).
T Carrier	A TDM digital transmission facility, usually PTT supplied, and usually operating at and aggregate rate of 1.544 Mbps and above.
T1	An AT&T term for a digital carrier facility, used to transmit a DS-1 formatted digital signal at 1.544 Mbps. T1C operates at 3.152 Mbps and T2 operates at 6.312 Mbps.
Tariff	A published service or equipment offering and related charging schedules provided by a specialised or common carrier.
TCP/IP	*Transmission Control Protocol / Internet Protocol.* A protocol specification used in ARPANET, that corresponds to layers three and four of the OSI model.

TDM	**Time Division Multiplexing.** A technique for sharing a single communications line among several data streams by dividing the channel capacity into time segments.
TDMA	**Time Division Multiple Access.** A synchronous TDM scheme which enables a number of transmitting devices to share a communication channel's capacity by allocating the total channel to each device in turn for a short amount of time.
Telecommunications	"Any transmission, emission or reception of signs, signals, writing, images and sounds or intelligence of any nature by wire, radio, optical or other electromagnetic systems" (ITU definition).
Telematics	User-oriented information transmission services, such as Teletex, Videotex and Facsimile.
Telemetry	The transmission of coded analogue data, often real time parameters (such as alarms or counters), from a remote site.
Teleprocessing	Remote access data processing; the use of data communications to accomplish a computer-based task.
Teleservice	A type of service provided by an ISDN which utilises ISDN bearer services to provide facilities such as Videotex or Facsimile.
Teletex	A new CCITT system for conveying documents by means of high-speed (2400 bps) data transmission, for example from one word processor to another; the intended successor to Telex.

Teletext	A generic simplex data transmission technique designed for widespread broadcasting of graphics and textual information, for display on subscriber televisions or terminals.
Telex	The public switched low-speed data network which is used worldwide for text transmission.
TOP	*Technical Office Protocol.* Developed by Boeing, has the same technical and economic aims as MAP, uses CSMA/CD and can interwork MAP and TOP with a simple bridging device.
Transmission	The sending of data to one or more locations or recipients.
Transmission Medium	The physical communications path between transmitters and receivers in a communications system.
Trunk	A single circuit between two points that has the capability to carry numerous channels; a circuit used to connect two switching centres, or a switching centre and a distribution point, such as a PBX.
V-Series Recommendations	The CCITT Recommendations for data transmission over analogue telephone networks.
Videotex	The term given by CCITT to cover viewdata and teletext.
Viewdata	A generic term for a system which displays information through a specifically adapted television set via a telephone line connection.
X-Series Recommendations	The CCITT Recommendations for data transmission over digital data networks.

Appendices

I-Series recommendations

I.461	Support of X.21 and X.21 bis based DTEs by an ISDN (X.30)
I.462	Support of packet mode terminal equipment by an ISDN (X.31)
I.463	Support of DTEs with V-series type interfaces by an ISDN (V110)
I.500	General Structure of ISDN Interworking
I.600	Maintenance Principles

V-Series standards

V.21	300 baud modem standardised for use on the switched telephone network
V.22	1200 bps full duplex, 2-wire modem standardised for use on the general switched telephone network
V.24	Physical Interface between DTEs and DCEs
V.32	Standard for full-duplex modems working at high speed over PSTN lines or leased lines
V.35	Standard for trunk interface between a network access device and a packet network

X-Series recommendations

X.1   International user classes of service in PDNs and ISDNs

X.2   International user facilities in public data networks

X.3   PAD facility in a public data network

X.10   Categories of access for DTEs to public data transmission services

X.20   Interface between DTE and DCE for start-stop transmission services on public data networks

X.21   Synchronous interface between DTEs and DCEs

X.21 bis   General purpose interface for V series devices

X.25   Packet mode interface between DTEs and DCEs

X.28   DTE/DCE interface for start-stop node DTE accessing the PAD facility on a PDN situated in the same country

X.29   Procedures for exchange of control information and user data between a packet mode DTE and a PAD facility

X.31   Support of packet mode terminals by an ISDN

X.32   Interface between DTE and DCE for terminal operating in the packet-mode and accessing a PSPDN through PSTN or an ISDN

X.75   Interface between packet switched data networks

Index